CW01023413

Introduction to Quantum Computing with Qiskit

Macauley Coggins

2021

Scarborough Quantum Computing Ltd

For discounts regarding bulk purchases of this textbook please email: mcoggins@quantumcomputinguk.org

ISBN 978-1-3999-1427-7

If you are not completely confused by quantum mechanics, you do not understand it

—John Wheeler

About the Author

Macauley Coggins

Macauley Coggins is a Software Developer, Researcher and Founder of Quantum Computing UK which aims to use quantum computing to solve real world problems.

Dear Reader!

Thank you very much for your interest in my textbook. I hope that you will find this textbook enlightening and that it will open up a whole new world for you in quantum computing

Kind Regards

Macauley Coggins

Contents

Contents

Contents

Contents

Contents

Contents

Notation

Greek Alphabet

α	alpha	ν	nu
β	beta	ξ	xi
γ	gamma	o	omicron
δ	delta	π	pi
ϵ	epsilon	ρ	rho
ζ	zeta	σ	sigma
η	eta	τ	tau
θ	theta	υ	upsilon
ι	iota	ϕ	phi
κ	kappa	χ	chi
λ	lambda	ψ	psi
μ	mu	ω	omega

Computational Basis states

$|0\rangle, |1\rangle$

Hadamard Basis states

$|-\rangle = \frac{|0\rangle - |1\rangle}{\sqrt{2}}$

$|+\rangle = \frac{|0\rangle + |1\rangle}{\sqrt{2}}$

Computational to Hadamard Basis

$|0\rangle \longrightarrow \frac{|0\rangle + |1\rangle}{\sqrt{2}}$

$|1\rangle \longrightarrow \frac{|0\rangle - |1\rangle}{\sqrt{2}}$

Pauli Gates

$X = \begin{bmatrix} 0 & 1 \\ 1 & 0 \end{bmatrix} Y = \begin{bmatrix} 0 & -i \\ i & 0 \end{bmatrix} Z = \begin{bmatrix} 1 & 0 \\ 0 & -1 \end{bmatrix}$

Hadamard Gate

$H = \frac{1}{\sqrt{2}} \begin{bmatrix} 1 & 1 \\ 1 & -1 \end{bmatrix}$

Rotational Gates

$RX(\theta) = \begin{bmatrix} cos(\frac{\theta}{2}) & -isin(\frac{\theta}{2}) \\ -isin(\frac{\theta}{2}) & cos(\frac{\theta}{2}) \end{bmatrix}$

$$RY(\theta) = \begin{bmatrix} \cos\theta & -\sin\theta \\ \sin\theta & \cos\theta) \end{bmatrix}$$

$$RZ(\lambda) = \begin{bmatrix} e^{-i\frac{\lambda}{2}} & 0 \\ 0 & e^{i\frac{\lambda}{2}} \end{bmatrix}$$

$$U1(\lambda) \begin{bmatrix} 1 & 0 \\ 0 & e^{i\lambda} \end{bmatrix}$$

$$U2(\phi,\lambda) = \frac{1}{\sqrt{2}} \begin{bmatrix} 1 & -e^{i\lambda} \\ e^{i\phi} & e^{i(\phi+\lambda)} \end{bmatrix}$$

$$U3(\theta,\phi,\lambda) = \begin{bmatrix} \cos(\theta) & -e^{i\lambda}\sin(\theta) \\ e^{i\phi}\sin(\theta) & e^{i(\phi+\lambda)}\cos(\theta) \end{bmatrix}$$

Other Single Qubit gates

$$S = \begin{bmatrix} 1 & 0 \\ 0 & i \end{bmatrix}$$

$$T = \begin{bmatrix} 1 & 0 \\ 0 & e^{i\pi/4} \end{bmatrix}$$

Multi-Qubit gates

$$CNOT = \begin{bmatrix} 1 & 0 & 0 & 0 \\ 0 & 1 & 0 & 0 \\ 0 & 0 & 0 & 1 \\ 0 & 0 & 1 & 0 \end{bmatrix}$$

$$\text{Toffoli} = \begin{bmatrix} 1 & 0 & 0 & 0 & 0 & 0 & 0 & 0 \\ 0 & 1 & 0 & 0 & 0 & 0 & 0 & 0 \\ 0 & 0 & 1 & 0 & 0 & 0 & 0 & 0 \\ 0 & 0 & 0 & 1 & 0 & 0 & 0 & 0 \\ 0 & 0 & 0 & 0 & 1 & 0 & 0 & 0 \\ 0 & 0 & 0 & 0 & 0 & 1 & 0 & 0 \\ 0 & 0 & 0 & 0 & 0 & 0 & 0 & 1 \\ 0 & 0 & 0 & 0 & 0 & 0 & 1 & 0 \end{bmatrix}$$

$$\text{Fredkin} = \begin{bmatrix} 1 & 0 & 0 & 0 & 0 & 0 & 0 & 0 \\ 0 & 1 & 0 & 0 & 0 & 0 & 0 & 0 \\ 0 & 0 & 1 & 0 & 0 & 0 & 0 & 0 \\ 0 & 0 & 0 & 1 & 0 & 0 & 0 & 0 \\ 0 & 0 & 0 & 0 & 1 & 0 & 0 & 0 \\ 0 & 0 & 0 & 0 & 0 & 0 & 1 & 0 \\ 0 & 0 & 0 & 0 & 0 & 1 & 0 & 0 \\ 0 & 0 & 0 & 0 & 0 & 0 & 0 & 1 \end{bmatrix}$$

$$\text{SWAP} = \begin{bmatrix} 1 & 0 & 0 & 0 \\ 0 & 0 & 1 & 0 \\ 0 & 1 & 0 & 0 \\ 0 & 0 & 0 & 1 \end{bmatrix}$$

$$\text{iSWAP} = \begin{bmatrix} 1 & 0 & 0 & 0 \\ 0 & 0 & i & 0 \\ 0 & i & 0 & 0 \\ 0 & 0 & 0 & 1 \end{bmatrix}$$

Contents

$$\text{Controlled Hadamard} = \begin{bmatrix} 1 & 0 & 0 & 0 \\ 0 & \frac{1}{\sqrt{2}} & 0 & \frac{1}{\sqrt{2}} \\ 0 & 0 & 1 & 0 \\ 0 & \frac{1}{\sqrt{2}} & 0 & -\frac{1}{\sqrt{2}} \end{bmatrix}$$

Preface

Quantum computing as a whole is a very fascinating yet complicated field. As such for a fresh beginner it can seem daunting. This book serves as a very gentle introduction to quantum computing which aims to be all encompassing and is divided in to two main sections.

The first section regards theory with the first chapters focusing as an introduction to quantum mechanics including a primer on quantum mechanical phenomenon such as quantum superposition and entanglement. Then the material will progress to quantum computing theory. Chapters 4 and 5 will introduce the reader to the qubit and information encoding using rotations and operations. Chapter 6 will introduce the reader to quantum logic gates starting with the Pauli gates and then on to rotational gates and multi-qubit gates. Chapter 7 and 8 will progress on to quantum circuits and quantum algorithms. The main algorithms discussed will be Grover's algorithm and Shor's algorithm. The next chapters will focus on quantum error correction/mitigation. The second half of the textbook pertains to programming quantum devices in Qiskit with the first chapters focusing on simple programs such as implementation of single logic gates. Later chapters will focus on implementation of quantum algorithms such was Shor's and Grovers and onward to quantum error correction/mitigation. Chapter 13 introduces the user to quantum hardware with a focus on superconducting quantum devices. Chapter 14 expands on this to describe the different qubit implementations. The second half of the textbook (chapter 15 onwards) introduces the user to Qiskit. This is a python library that allows users to write programs for IBM quantum computers. The first chapters of this section aim to help the user get started with Qiskit. Then the chapters progress on to creating gate level programs with quantum logic gates. The programs will get more complex progressing from logic gate implementations to quantum error correction and machine learning.

1 Introduction

While current classical computers as we know them today have their routes back in the 1940s the idea of computers that could harness quantum mechanics to solve certain problems were envisioned relatively recently. Indeed while quantum mechanics was in the past largely ignored it now plays an important role across different industries from the design of integrated circuits through to the design of lasers and optics.

In 1980 Paul Benioff published what could be proposed as the first paper linking computing to quantum mechanics [1]. More specifically his paper described a quantum mechanical model for a Turing Machine. A Turing Machine is an abstract computational device capable of computing any algorithm. It consists of an infinitely long tape consisting of cells that can be read or written to by a tape head. The tape head will write 1 or 0 based upon its present state and then move to the right or leftmost cell. States for the Turing machine are defined in a finite state table. For example if the present state is A and the tape head reads 0 it may write 1 and move to the rightmost cell. If instead the tape head reads 1 it will write 0 and go to the cell to the left.

Benioffs paper instead described a quantum mechanical model where the tape is replaced by a lattice of quantum spin systems of finite length. Computations on these quantum spin systems would be done by evolving the Hamiltonian of the system based upon the initial states and by predefined rules.

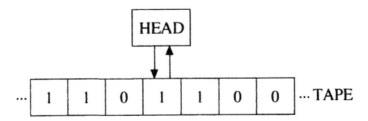

Figure 1.1: Diagram of a Turing Machine

However it is important to note that the computations done using this model are classical and thus can actually be simulated by a classical Turing Machine.

In 1982 Richard Feynman published a paper where he proposed using a quantum computer to simulate physics [9]. In the paper he describes the difficulties involved in simulating quantum physics using classical computers. As such he argues that a quantum computers would be a better alternative. This is a wonderful paper which I definitely recommend the reader to take a look at.

In 1985 David Deutsch presented a model for a universal quantum computer which is capable of perfectly simulating every finite, realizable physical system [7]. In the paper the universal quantum computer is described as having two main components. A finite processor and an infinite memory of which corresponds to the infinitely long tape in a Turing machine. While the proposed model could simulate any operation that a Turing machine could it instead differs by memory cells in to a linear superposition of states. Superposition is a important phenomenon in quantum mechanics which will be discussing in later sections.

Up to this point quantum computers were theoretical as none had been created up to this point. However this did not stop researchers from developing algorithms that could be ran on quantum computers to solve specific problems. One of the most famous examples is Shor's algorithm which was developed by Peter Shor in 1994 [17]. This was an algorithm developed to factor integers which sounds incredibly trivial but has profound implications as all of modern encryption is based upon factoring. Furthermore using this algorithm a quantum computer could potentially factor integers much faster than any classical computer.

In 1996 Lov Grover published a paper detailing a quantum algorithm for database search. Today known as Grover's algorithm this made use of quantum mechanics to do a database search in only $O(\sqrt{N})$ steps while a classical algorithm will take at the least O(N) steps. We will explore both Shor's and Grover's algorithm including how to implement them both in Qiskit.

Now let me stress that no feasible quantum computer had been developed up to this point so lets now focus on the history concerning the physical development of quantum computers up to the present day. In 1998 the first ever quantum algorithm to be physically demonstrated on a quantum computer was accomplished [11]. The quantum computer consisted of only two qubits. It used an NMR setup which works by using the spin states found in atomic nuclei. The algorithm used on the computer is called Deutsch's algorithm which sets out to find if a function is balanced or constant. We will explore this algorithm later in the chapter on quantum algorithms. Later in the same year the same team successfully implemented Grover's search using an NMR setup [12]. While NMR based setups were the first they came with their own problems. For one none of the experiments implemented quantum entanglement between qubits [6]. Quantum entanglement is one of the two quantum phenomenon that quantum computers take advantage (the other being quantum superposition). Both phenomenon will be explored thoroughly in the next chapter. The next landmark development was a paper by Nakamura et al which showed how qubits could be implemented using Superconducting circuits [14]. This is the basis for superconducting quantum computing which is used today by the likes of IBM and Google. After this the physical development of quantum computers slowly progressed with new technologies and architectures being introduced over time.

In 2011 a company called D-Wave introduced what could be described as the worlds first commercial quantum computer: the D-Wave One. This was a quantum annealing processor consisting of 128 superconducting flux qubits. It is important to note though that this was a massive surprise or more so a leap from the environment at the time. In 2011 all quantum devices were highly experimental and only had a few number of qubits. Then suddenly D-Wave shows up with a 128 qubit processor ready to be sold. There was a lot of skepticism around the processor to the point where peers wondered if the processor was even quantum at all. It turned out it did make use of quantum mechanics but because the processor used quantum annealing it was restricted to solving a class of problems known as optimisation problems. Another big question was does the processor provide a quantum advantage? That is can the processor solve these optimisation problems faster than a classical computer? Well the answer to that was very mixed. One study by Boixo et al showed that there was strong evidence the processor used quantum annealing [5]. However the study also showed suboptimal annealing times for the problems tested. Furthermore the annealing times on the processor were slightly slower than a classical annealer running on an 8-core Intel Xeon E5-2670 CPU and on an Nvidia K20X GPU. However this was one study and looking back at the literature concerning the performance of the D-Wave One the results seemed to be more mixed. In 2012 researchers used the processor to solve a lattice protein folding problem [16]. That same year the D-Wave One was used to determine Ramsay numbers [4]. This used 84 qubits and was the largest implementation of adiabatic quantum computing at the time. Over the years D-Wave has released more powerful processors. In 2013 they released the D-Wave Two with 512 qubits. In 2015 they released the D-Wave 2000Q with 2040 qubits. As of writing their latest processor the D-Wave Advantage boasts 5060 qubits. However it is best to remember that even though these processors boast a massive number of qubits they are still based on quantum annealing and as such can only really be used for optimisation problems such as the Travelling Salesman problem.

Over the last couple of years the number of companies putting their hats in to the ring has exploded dramatically. Big players such as IBM and Google are rushing to create their own universal quantum computers. These differ from D-Waves processors in that they are not based on adiabatic quantum computing or quantum annealing . Instead they use superconducting qubits to implement the quantum gate model. The quantum gate model is where quantum computers do computations using quantum logic gates. We will explore the quantum gate model in depth in later chapters.

2 Quantum mechanics and associated phenomena

Before we dive in to quantum computing we first need to take a look at quantum mechanics as this is what quantum computers take advantage of in order to do computations. Quantum mechanics is a fundamental theory that describes the behaviour of the very small including atoms and subatomic particles . In quantum mechanics particles and their properties take on discrete values. For example light is made up of discrete wave packets called photons .

2.1 The Ultraviolet catastrophe

Before the discovery of the photon it was believed that electromagnetic radiation was made up of waves. However a number of experiments seemed to counter this notion. In the early 19th century scientists were interested in how black bodies absorb and emit electromagnetic radiation. A black body is simply an object that absorbs all radiation regardless of frequency. However when in thermal equilibrium it can emit radiation called black body radiation. Emission of thermal radiation from a black body was believed to follow Rayleigh–Jeans law which describes the spectral radiance of radiation as a function of its frequency.

$$B_v(T) = \frac{2v^2 k_B T}{c^2} \tag{2.1}$$

Where v is the frequency, T is the temperature in kelvins, c is the speed of light and k_B is the Boltzmann constant.

For very high frequencies this law holds up. However it broke down for frequencies towards the ultraviolet range as it predicted that the amount energy would tend to infinity. This did not hold up with experimental observations. In 1900 Max Planck attempted to address this discrepancy by making the assumption that electromagnetic radiation was absorbed or emitted in discrete wave packets. This assumption agreed with experimental observations and accurately predicted the spectral radiance of radiation for higher frequencies in which the Rayleigh–Jeans law failed.

2.2 The Photoelectric effect

Another issue with the notion of electromagnetic radiation being a wave was with the photoelectric effect. The photoelectric effect is where if light is absorbed by a metal the atoms become ionized and an electron is emitted. However because light was thought to be a wave the amount of electrons emitted should increase as the intensity of the light increased. In 1905 Albert Einstein showed that this was not the case. In his experiment he shined light consisting of different frequencies and intensities at a metal. This was to see at what frequency and intensity electrons could be emitted from the metal. What he found was remarkable, if he shined light with a lower frequency and low intensity no electrons would be emitted from the metal. If the

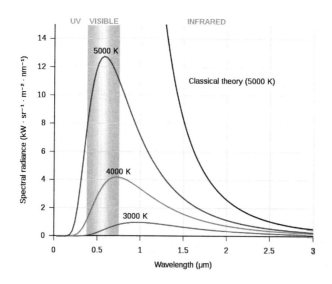

Figure 2.1: Spectral radiance as a function of frequency.

light was high intensity but low frequency then again no electrons were emitted. However if he shined high frequency light but with even a low intensity the electrons would be emitted. This was a problem as it meant that electron emission was a function of the frequency and not based on the intensity as it should be if light is only a wave. However if light was instead a discrete wave-packet with energy proportional to its frequency then this would make sense. A higher frequency photon would have enough energy to ionize an atom whereas a lower frequency photon would not. This discovery led to Albert Einstein winning the Nobel Prize for physics in 1921.

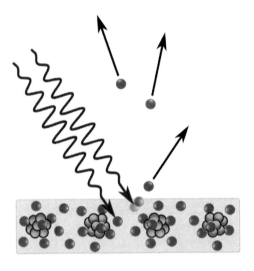

Figure 2.2: Photoelectric effect

2.3 The Double-slit experiment

So is light a wave or a particle? Well the simple answer is that it carries properties of both. A very good demonstration of this is with the Double-slit experiment. The experiment consists of a light source that shines on a plate consisting of two slits. The light will pass through the slits on to a back screen where there will be an interference pattern due to the wave like nature of light. However we know that light is made up of photons and is not purely a wave so this interference pattern does not make sense if light is made up on photons! If we instead use a single photon source so that only one photon after another is hitting the screen you will see that they will hit random places and after enough have hit the screen an interference pattern will start to emerge. This is a very concrete demonstration of a quantum mechanical phenomenon wave-particle duality where quantum particles such as photons or electrons can have the properties of both a wave and a particle.

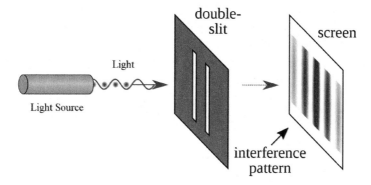

Figure 2.3: Diagram of the Double-slit experiment

2.4 Quantum Superposition

Quantum superposition is the ability of a quantum particle to occupy multiple states at any given time. For example consider a photon. A photon has a property called polarization which is simply the orientation of its oscillations. In a photon the polarization can be either vertical or horizontal. Both polarizations can be described as state vectors for example vertical polarization can be denoted as $|\uparrow\rangle$ and horizontal polarization as $|\rightarrow\rangle$.

2 Quantum mechanics and associated phenomena

It is important to note that both states have a difference in orientation of $90°$. However due to superposition it can be both vertical and horizontal at the same time such that the state is $|\psi\rangle = \frac{1}{\sqrt{2}}|\uparrow\rangle + \frac{1}{\sqrt{2}}|\rightarrow\rangle$. Note that a superposition of $|\uparrow\rangle$ and $|\rightarrow\rangle$ is $45°$ on the unit circle such that its orientation is in between $|\uparrow\rangle$ and $|\rightarrow\rangle$! A quantum particle can exhibit a phenomenon called wave-function collapse where the superposition will collapse in to one of the states that make up that superposition when the particle is measured. For example if a photon is in a superposition such that $|\psi\rangle = \frac{1}{\sqrt{2}}|\uparrow\rangle + \frac{1}{\sqrt{2}}|\rightarrow\rangle$ then the photons state will become either $|\uparrow\rangle$ or $|\rightarrow\rangle$ with equal probability.

2.5 Quantum Entanglement

Quantum entanglement is where two quantum particles are entangled such that the state of one particle cannot be described without the other. Entanglement also means that if one of the particles states changes then the other particles state will change too. This phenomena is used in quantum computers to change the states of qubits based on the states of other qubits. For example say we have two entangled photons called A and B and we measure photon A's polarity such that it becomes $|\rightarrow\rangle$. Because both photons are entangled photon B's state will become $|\rightarrow\rangle$ too. On the other hand they may be anti-correlated where if one photon is measured then the second photon will have the opposite state, For example if photon A's polarity is measured such that it is $|\rightarrow\rangle$ then photon B will become $|\uparrow\rangle$. It is important to note that entanglement can happen between particles even if there is a large distance between them and in some experiments it can seem to be instantaneous. In 2008 scientists performed an experiment where it was found non-locality to be at least 20,000 faster than the speed of light. However quantum entanglement cannot be used to send information faster than light due to the non-communication theorem.

3 Quantum Computing

Now that we have covered quantum mechanics we can finally get in to the theory of quantum computing including how information is encoded and manipulated. As explained earlier in the book quantum computers are computers that make use of quantum mechanical phenomena in order to do computations. On quantum computers information is encoded on a unit of information called a qubit. In the gate model architecture of quantum computing computations are done by applying operations to qubits via quantum logic gates.

3.1 The Qubit

Before we discuss the qubit in detail it is best to first explain how a classical bit works. A classical bit is what classical computers (those used in everyday life) use to encode information. The bit only has two states "0" and "1". Because of its simplicity a bit can be implemented in many different ways. For example in computer logic a "1" is normally a high voltage and "0" a low voltage. In fibre optics the two states can be encoded as light or darkness and in hard drives it can be different directions in magnetization.

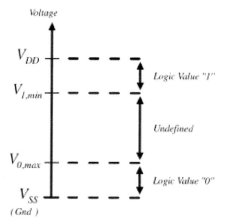

Figure 3.1: Voltage levels for a bit

As you can see from the figure above the states of a classical bit in digital logic is simply a scalar value based on the voltage. For "0" it is any voltage between Gnd (Ground) and $V_{0,max}$ which is the maximum voltage for "0". For "1" the voltage range is between $V_{1,min}$ and $V_{1,max}$

Quantum computers represent information differently with a unit of information called the qubit or quantum bit. Whereas a classical bit is based on a scalar value (such as voltage) a qubit encodes states as a unit vector with a magnitude of 1 and a direction. A qubit can hold a 1, 0, or a superposition of both much like quantum particles discussed in the chapter on quantum mechanics. Because qubit states are vectors we have to introduce a form of notation for vectors called Dirac notation. In Dirac notation we use a vertical bar and an angle bracket (also known as a ket) $|\rangle$. For example a logical "1" on a qubit in

33

ket notation is $|1\rangle$ and a logical "0" is $|0\rangle$. From now on we will be using this notation for all qubit states. Note that in quantum computing $|0\rangle$ and $|1\rangle$ are together known as the computational basis states.

Quantum states can also be represented using column vectors . For example $|0\rangle$ can be represented using the column vector:

$$|0\rangle = \begin{bmatrix} 1 \\ 0 \end{bmatrix} \tag{3.1}$$

and $|1\rangle$ can be represented as:

$$|1\rangle = \begin{bmatrix} 0 \\ 1 \end{bmatrix} \tag{3.2}$$

As highlighted earlier qubits can be in a superposition of $|0\rangle$ and $|1\rangle$ so how is a superposition represented? Well that depends on what initial state the qubit was in before putting it in to superposition. For example if the qubit was originally $|0\rangle$ then the state will become:

$$|0\rangle \rightarrow \frac{|0\rangle + |1\rangle}{\sqrt{2}} = \frac{1}{\sqrt{2}} \begin{bmatrix} 1 \\ 1 \end{bmatrix} \tag{3.3}$$

which can also be represented more compactly as $|+\rangle$

$$|1\rangle \rightarrow \frac{|0\rangle - |1\rangle}{\sqrt{2}} = \frac{1}{\sqrt{2}} \begin{bmatrix} 1 \\ -1 \end{bmatrix} \tag{3.4}$$

Which can be written as $|-\rangle$

When in superposition there is an equal probability of $|0\rangle$ or $|1\rangle$ being measured. This can be seen quite clearly from the state vectors above:

$$\frac{1}{\sqrt{2}}\begin{bmatrix}1\\1\end{bmatrix} = \begin{bmatrix}0.70710678118\\0.70710678118\end{bmatrix} \tag{3.5}$$

Note that the probability of a state being measured is the square of the state amplitude:

$$0.70710678118^2 = 0.5 \tag{3.6}$$

From this we can see that the probability of a state being measured when in superposition is 0.5 or 50%

Here is a useful list of column vectors and their corresponding states:

$$|0\rangle = \begin{bmatrix}1\\0\end{bmatrix} \tag{3.7}$$

$$|1\rangle = \begin{bmatrix}0\\1\end{bmatrix} \tag{3.8}$$

$$-|0\rangle = \begin{bmatrix}-1\\0\end{bmatrix} \tag{3.9}$$

$$-|1\rangle = \begin{bmatrix}0\\-1\end{bmatrix} \tag{3.10}$$

$$|+\rangle = \frac{|0\rangle + |1\rangle}{\sqrt{2}} = \frac{1}{\sqrt{2}}\begin{bmatrix}1\\1\end{bmatrix} \tag{3.11}$$

$$|-\rangle = \frac{|0\rangle - |1\rangle}{\sqrt{2}} = \frac{1}{\sqrt{2}}\begin{bmatrix}1\\-1\end{bmatrix} \tag{3.12}$$

Column vectors will be very useful when we discuss about matrix representations of quantum logic gates a little later.

4 Qubit representation with the Bloch sphere

A qubit and its states can be hard to mentally visualise. However one easy way to visualise a qubit is with a geometric representation known as the . So what is the Bloch sphere? Simply put it represents the qubit as a sphere where the computational states $|0\rangle$ and $|1\rangle$ are on the poles of the sphere. However it is important to note that a qubits state can be at any point on the surface of the sphere. For example in the figure the qubits state can be seen as the vector $|\psi\rangle$. When a qubit is put in to superposition the qubits state will end up on the equator of the sphere ($|+\rangle$ and $|-\rangle$ are at opposite sides of the equator).

Operations on the qubit can be thought of as rotations on this sphere. For example there is a set of quantum logic gates called the Pauli gates that do a rotation of 180 degrees (π radians) each on a specific axis of the sphere. A Pauli X gate will do rotation of 180 degrees on the X-axis of the bloch sphere. While a Z-gate is a rotation of 180 degrees on the Z-axis. The Y-gate follows this pattern by rotating the state 180 degrees around the Y-axis. As well as rotations on the X,Y,Z axis rotations can be denoted using the spherical coordinate system. With the spherical coordinate system we can denote any rotation using the values θ and φ. Where θ rotates around the computational basis of the qubit and φ rotates the phase of the qubit. For example using the coordinate system an X-gate would be a rotation of θ by 180

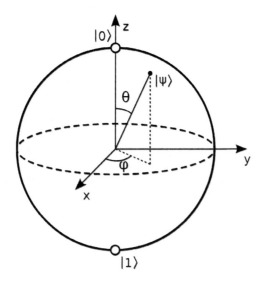

Figure 4.1: Bloch sphere

degrees while a Z-gate would be a rotation of φ by 180 degrees.

5 Quantum logic gates

Logic gates are used to do operations on qubits. There are many different types of qubits but they all essentially boil down in to doing a rotation around the qubit by a specific amount and in a specific direction. Some logic gates act on only one qubit (called single qubit gates) while other gates act on multiple qubits (multi-qubit gates).

5.1 Pauli gates

5.1.1 Pauli X Gate

A Pauli X gate (also known as a NOT gate) corresponds to a rotation of 180 degrees (π radians) along the X axis of the Bloch sphere. This means that the state of the qubit is flipped from $|1\rangle$ to $|0\rangle$ or vice versa.

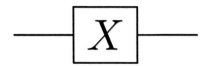

Figure 5.1: Circuit representation of an X gate

38

5 Quantum logic gates

Each quantum logic gate will have a corresponding unitary matrix. These matrices are a compact way of describing the operation of the logic gate. For example the Pauli-X gate is described by the matrix:

$$X = \begin{bmatrix} 0 & 1 \\ 1 & 0 \end{bmatrix} \tag{5.1}$$

Using this matrix we can find out how this gate will affect the qubits state by multiplying the matrix by the column vector of the qubits state. For example if our qubits state is $|0\rangle$ then its column vector is $\begin{bmatrix} 1 \\ 0 \end{bmatrix}$ which we multiply by the Pauli-X matrix:

$$\begin{bmatrix} 0 & 1 \\ 1 & 0 \end{bmatrix} \begin{bmatrix} 1 \\ 0 \end{bmatrix} = \begin{bmatrix} 0(1) + 1(0) \\ 1(1) + 0(0) \end{bmatrix} = \begin{bmatrix} 0 \\ 1 \end{bmatrix} = |1\rangle \tag{5.2}$$

From this we can see that the Pauli X gate will flip the qubit from $|0\rangle$ to $|1\rangle$.

If we first initialise the qubit to $|1\rangle$ and multiply by the Pauli X gate:

$$\begin{bmatrix} 0 & 1 \\ 1 & 0 \end{bmatrix} \begin{bmatrix} 0 \\ 1 \end{bmatrix} = \begin{bmatrix} 0(0) + 1(1) \\ 1(0) + 0(1) \end{bmatrix} = \begin{bmatrix} 1 \\ 0 \end{bmatrix} = |0\rangle \tag{5.3}$$

Which is correct as the qubit has flipped from $|1\rangle$ to $|0\rangle$.

5.1.2 Pauli Y Gate

A Pauli Y gateis a rotation of 180 degrees (π radians) around the Y axis of the bloch sphere.This will map $|0\rangle$ to $i|1\rangle$ and $|1\rangle$ to $-i|0\rangle$

The matrix for the Y gate is as follows:

$$Y = \begin{bmatrix} 0 & -i \\ i & 0 \end{bmatrix} \tag{5.4}$$

Figure 5.2: Circuit diagram of a Y gate

Like with the Pauli X gate we can multiply the column vector associated with the qubits state by the Pauli Y matrix to see how it affects the qubit. For example let's initialise the qubits state to $|0\rangle$ and multiply it by the Pauli Y matrix:

$$\begin{bmatrix} 0 & -i \\ i & 0 \end{bmatrix} \begin{bmatrix} 1 \\ 0 \end{bmatrix} = \begin{bmatrix} 0(1) + -i(0) \\ i(1) + 0(0) \end{bmatrix} = \begin{bmatrix} 0 \\ i \end{bmatrix} \tag{5.5}$$

which is correct as the resulting column vector is for $i|1\rangle$. If we instead initialise the qubit to $|1\rangle$:

$$\begin{bmatrix} 0 & -i \\ i & 0 \end{bmatrix} \begin{bmatrix} 0 \\ 1 \end{bmatrix} = \begin{bmatrix} 0(0) + -i(1) \\ i(0) + 0(1) \end{bmatrix} = \begin{bmatrix} -i \\ 0 \end{bmatrix} \tag{5.6}$$

Which is correct as the column vector is for $-i|0\rangle$

5.1.3 Pauli Z Gate

A Z gate flips the phase of the qubit by performing a rotation of 180 degrees around the Z axis of the qubit. This maps $|1\rangle$ to $-|1\rangle$ but leaves $|0\rangle$ unchanged.

The matrix for the Z-gate is as follows:

$$Z = \begin{bmatrix} 1 & 0 \\ 0 & -1 \end{bmatrix} \tag{5.7}$$

We can see how the Pauli-Z gate operates on the qubit by multiplying the column vector of the qubits state by the Pauli-Z matrix. For example let's initialise the qubit to $|0\rangle$:

$$\begin{bmatrix} 1 & 0 \\ 0 & -1 \end{bmatrix} \begin{bmatrix} 1 \\ 0 \end{bmatrix} = \begin{bmatrix} 1(1) + 0(0) \\ 0(1) + -1(0) \end{bmatrix} = \begin{bmatrix} 1 \\ 0 \end{bmatrix} \tag{5.8}$$

Which is correct as it has left $|0\rangle$ unchanged. Now let's initialise the qubit to $|1\rangle$ and see how the Z gate transforms the qubits state:

$$\begin{bmatrix} 1 & 0 \\ 0 & -1 \end{bmatrix} \begin{bmatrix} 0 \\ 1 \end{bmatrix} = \begin{bmatrix} 1(0) + 0(1) \\ 0(0) + -1(1) \end{bmatrix} = \begin{bmatrix} 0 \\ -1 \end{bmatrix} \tag{5.9}$$

Which is correct as it has changed the qubits state from $|1\rangle$ to $-|1\rangle$

Figure 5.3: Circuit diagram of a Z gate

5.1.4 Identity Gate

The Identity gate is a very simple gate that does nothing and leaves the qubits states unchanged. The matrix for the identity gate is as follows:

$$I = \begin{bmatrix} 1 & 0 \\ 0 & 1 \end{bmatrix} \tag{5.10}$$

To see how useless the Identity gate is let's multiply the qubits state by the identity gates matrix.

If we initialise the qubits state to $|0\rangle$:

$$\begin{bmatrix} 1 & 0 \\ 0 & 1 \end{bmatrix} \begin{bmatrix} 1 \\ 0 \end{bmatrix} = \begin{bmatrix} 1(1) + 0(0) \\ 0(1) + 1(0) \end{bmatrix} = \begin{bmatrix} 1 \\ 0 \end{bmatrix} \tag{5.11}$$

Which has left $|0\rangle$ unchanged.

If we initialise the qubits state to $|1\rangle$:

$$\begin{bmatrix} 1 & 0 \\ 0 & 1 \end{bmatrix} \begin{bmatrix} 0 \\ 1 \end{bmatrix} = \begin{bmatrix} 1(0) + 0(1) \\ 0(0) + 1(1) \end{bmatrix} = \begin{bmatrix} 0 \\ 1 \end{bmatrix} \tag{5.12}$$

Which has left $|1\rangle$ unchanged.

5.2 Hadamard gate

A Hadamard gate is one of the most important gates in quantum computing. Simply put it puts a qubit in to superposition of states such that if the qubit is $|0\rangle$ then the state will become:

$$|0\rangle \longrightarrow \frac{|0\rangle + |1\rangle}{\sqrt{2}} \tag{5.13}$$

and if it was $|1\rangle$ then the state will become:

$$|1\rangle \longrightarrow \frac{|0\rangle - |1\rangle}{\sqrt{2}} \tag{5.14}$$

In terms of rotations this corresponds to a rotation of π (180 degrees) around the Z-axis followed by $\frac{\pi}{2}$ (90 degrees) around the Y-axis. This means that the pure state will be on the equator of the bloch sphere . Note that if the state is $|0\rangle$ then the resulting pure state will be on the equator (known as $|+\rangle$) but if it is $|1\rangle$ then it will be on the opposite side of the equator (known as $|-\rangle$).

The matrix for the Hadamard gate is as follows:

$$H = \tfrac{1}{\sqrt{2}} \begin{bmatrix} 1 & 1 \\ 1 & -1 \end{bmatrix} \tag{5.15}$$

If we initialise the qubit to $|0\rangle$ and apply a Hadamard gate:

$$\frac{1}{\sqrt{2}} \begin{bmatrix} 1 & 1 \\ 1 & -1 \end{bmatrix} \begin{bmatrix} 1 \\ 0 \end{bmatrix} = \frac{1}{\sqrt{2}} \begin{bmatrix} 1(1) + 1(0) \\ 1(1) + -1(0) \end{bmatrix} \tag{5.16}$$

$$= \frac{1}{\sqrt{2}} \begin{bmatrix} 1 \\ 1 \end{bmatrix} \tag{5.17}$$

Which has mapped $|0\rangle \longrightarrow \frac{|0\rangle + |1\rangle}{\sqrt{2}}$

Like the Pauli gates the Hadamard gate is reversible. Meaning that if we apply two Hadamard gates to a qubit we will get the previous state back!

$$\frac{1}{\sqrt{2}} \begin{bmatrix} 1 & 1 \\ 1 & -1 \end{bmatrix} \begin{bmatrix} 1 \\ 0 \end{bmatrix} = \frac{1}{\sqrt{2}} \begin{bmatrix} 1(1) + 1(0) \\ 1(1) + -1(-0) \end{bmatrix} \tag{5.18}$$

$$= \frac{1}{\sqrt{2}} \begin{bmatrix} 1 \\ 1 \end{bmatrix} \tag{5.19}$$

Now lets apply the second Hadamard gate

$$\frac{1}{\sqrt{2}} \begin{bmatrix} 1 & 1 \\ 1 & -1 \end{bmatrix} \frac{1}{\sqrt{2}} \begin{bmatrix} 1 \\ 1 \end{bmatrix} = \left(\frac{1}{\sqrt{2}}\right)^2 \begin{bmatrix} 1(1) + 1(1) \\ 1(1) + -1(1) \end{bmatrix} = \left(\frac{1}{\sqrt{2}}\right)^2 \begin{bmatrix} 2 \\ 0 \end{bmatrix} = \begin{bmatrix} 1 \\ 0 \end{bmatrix} \tag{5.20}$$

If we instead initialise the qubit to $|1\rangle$ and apply a Hadamard gate:

$$\frac{1}{\sqrt{2}} \begin{bmatrix} 1 & 1 \\ 1 & -1 \end{bmatrix} \begin{bmatrix} 0 \\ 1 \end{bmatrix} = \frac{1}{\sqrt{2}} \begin{bmatrix} 1(0) + 1(1) \\ 1(0) + -1(1) \end{bmatrix} = \frac{1}{\sqrt{2}} \begin{bmatrix} 1 \\ -1 \end{bmatrix} \tag{5.21}$$

Which has mapped $|1\rangle \longrightarrow \frac{|0\rangle - |1\rangle}{\sqrt{2}}$

Now lets see what happens when we apply another Hadamard gate:

$$\frac{1}{\sqrt{2}} \begin{bmatrix} 1 & 1 \\ 1 & -1 \end{bmatrix} \frac{1}{\sqrt{2}} \begin{bmatrix} 1 \\ -1 \end{bmatrix} = \left(\frac{1}{\sqrt{2}}\right)^2 \begin{bmatrix} 1(1) + 1(-1) \\ 1(1) + -1(-1) \end{bmatrix} \tag{5.22}$$

$$= \left(\frac{1}{\sqrt{2}}\right)^2 \begin{bmatrix} 0 \\ 2 \end{bmatrix} = \begin{bmatrix} 0 \\ 1 \end{bmatrix} \tag{5.23}$$

From this we can see that applying two Hadamard gates will revert the qubit back to its original state.

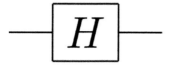

Figure 5.4: Circuit diagram of a Hadamard gate

Hadamard gate identities

As explained before when a Hadamard gate is applied to a qubit it puts the qubit in to a superposition of states. However because a Hadamard gate is essentially a mixture of rotations on the Z and Y axis you can get some surprising behaviour.

For example let's say if you initialize a qubit to $|0\rangle$ and then apply a Hadamard gate the qubit will be in a superposition of states such that when measured the qubit could be $|0\rangle$ or $|1\rangle$ with equal probability. However if we apply two Hadamard gates and measure the qubit the measurement will be $|0\rangle$. This is because two Hadamard gates applied to a qubit add up to a 360 degree rotation around the Z-axis and a 180 degree rotation around the Y axis. Simply put this means that if we apply two Hadamard gates then the state of the qubit remains unchanged.

So we have the identity: $HH = I$ where I is the identity gate.

5.2.1 S Gate

The S gate (otherwise known as the $\sqrt{Z}$ gate) is a gate that performs a rotation of $\frac{\pi}{2}$ around the Bloch sphere. It is represented by the following matrix:

$$S = \begin{bmatrix} 1 & 0 \\ 0 & i \end{bmatrix} \tag{5.24}$$

Much like the Z gate if we initialise the qubit to $|0\rangle$ and apply an S gate the qubits state will remain $|0\rangle$:

$$\begin{bmatrix} 1 & 0 \\ 0 & i \end{bmatrix}\begin{bmatrix} 1 \\ 0 \end{bmatrix} = \begin{bmatrix} 1(1) + 0(0) \\ 0(1) + i(0) \end{bmatrix} = \begin{bmatrix} 1 \\ 0 \end{bmatrix} \tag{5.25}$$

Where $\begin{bmatrix} 1 \\ 0 \end{bmatrix}$ is the column vector for $|0\rangle$

However if we first initialise the qubits state to $|1\rangle$:

$$\begin{bmatrix} 1 & 0 \\ 0 & i \end{bmatrix}\begin{bmatrix} 0 \\ 1 \end{bmatrix} = \begin{bmatrix} 1(0) + 0(1) \\ 0(0) + i(1) \end{bmatrix} = \begin{bmatrix} 0 \\ i \end{bmatrix} \tag{5.26}$$

It is important to note that since the S gate performs a rotation of $\frac{\pi}{2}$ if we apply two S gates we will get the equivalent of a Z gate:

$$\begin{bmatrix} 1 & 0 \\ 0 & i \end{bmatrix}\begin{bmatrix} 0 \\ 1 \end{bmatrix} = \begin{bmatrix} 1(0) + 0(1) \\ 0(0) + i(1) \end{bmatrix} = \begin{bmatrix} 0 \\ i \end{bmatrix} \tag{5.27}$$

$$\begin{bmatrix} 1 & 0 \\ 0 & i \end{bmatrix}\begin{bmatrix} 0 \\ i \end{bmatrix} = \begin{bmatrix} 1(0) + 0(i) \\ 0(0) + i(i) \end{bmatrix} = \begin{bmatrix} 0 \\ -1 \end{bmatrix} \tag{5.28}$$

Which is correct as if we applied a Z gate to $|1\rangle$ we would get $-|1\rangle$ whose column vector is $\begin{bmatrix} 0 \\ -1 \end{bmatrix}$

Note that the S gate differs from other logic gates in that it is not its own inverse. As such applying two S gates will not equal the identity of the qubits state.

5.2.2 T Gate

The T gate is a gate that performs a rotation around the Z axis by $\frac{\pi}{4}$. It is represented by the following matrix:

$$T = \begin{bmatrix} 1 & 0 \\ 0 & e^{i\frac{\pi}{4}} \end{bmatrix} \tag{5.29}$$

Much like the S gate and Z gate if we initialise the qubit to $|0\rangle$ and apply a T gate the qubits state will remain unchanged:

Where $|0\rangle$ and its associated column vector is $\begin{bmatrix} 1 \\ 0 \end{bmatrix}$

$$\begin{bmatrix} 1 & 0 \\ 0 & e^{i\frac{\pi}{4}} \end{bmatrix} \begin{bmatrix} 1 \\ 0 \end{bmatrix} = \begin{bmatrix} 1(1) + 0(0) \\ 0(1) + e^{i\frac{\pi}{4}}(0) \end{bmatrix} = \begin{bmatrix} 1 \\ 0 \end{bmatrix} \tag{5.30}$$

Now lets see what happens if we initialise the qubit to $|1\rangle$ and then apply a T gate:

$$\begin{bmatrix} 1 & 0 \\ 0 & e^{i\frac{\pi}{4}} \end{bmatrix} \begin{bmatrix} 0 \\ 1 \end{bmatrix} = \begin{bmatrix} 1(0) + 0(1) \\ 0(0) + e^{i\frac{\pi}{4}}(1) \end{bmatrix} = \begin{bmatrix} 0 \\ 0.707106781 + 0.707106781i \end{bmatrix}$$
$$\tag{5.31}$$

If the T gate was applied 4 times the resulting qubits state would be $\begin{bmatrix} 0 \\ -1 \end{bmatrix}$ which is the column vector for $-|1\rangle$. As such 4 T gates applied are the equivalent of a Z gate.

5.3 Rotation gates

The Pauli gates in the last section each did a rotation by 180 degrees in a specific axis. However qubit rotations can be in any amount. In qiskit specific rotations can be done by the RX, RZ and RY gates. There's also a universal single qubit gate which will be discussed called the U3 gate.

5.3.1 RX Gate

A RX gate is a gate that does a rotation around the X-axis by a specified amount which is normally denoted by θ.

$$RX = \begin{bmatrix} \cos\frac{\theta}{2} & -\sin\frac{\theta}{2} \\ -\sin\frac{\theta}{2} & \cos\frac{\theta}{2} \end{bmatrix} \tag{5.32}$$

Using the matrix multiplication we can see how the RX gate operates on the qubits state. For our first example lets initialise the qubits state to $|0\rangle$ and set θ to be π. This should flip the qubits state from $|0\rangle$ to $-|1\rangle$:

$$\begin{bmatrix} \cos\frac{\pi}{2} & -\sin\frac{\pi}{2} \\ -\sin\frac{\pi}{2} & \cos\frac{\pi}{2} \end{bmatrix} \begin{bmatrix} 1 \\ 0 \end{bmatrix} = \begin{bmatrix} (\cos\frac{\pi}{2})1 + (-\sin\frac{\pi}{2})0 \\ (-\sin\frac{\pi}{2})1 + (\cos\frac{\pi}{2})0 \end{bmatrix} = \begin{bmatrix} 0 \\ -1 \end{bmatrix} \tag{5.33}$$

Which is correct as the column vector $\begin{bmatrix} 0 \\ -1 \end{bmatrix} = -|1\rangle$

If we instead initialise the qubit to $|1\rangle$:

$$\begin{bmatrix} \cos\frac{\pi}{2} & -\sin\frac{\pi}{2} \\ -\sin\frac{\pi}{2} & \cos\frac{\pi}{2} \end{bmatrix} \begin{bmatrix} 0 \\ 1 \end{bmatrix} = \begin{bmatrix} (\cos\frac{\pi}{2})0 + (-\sin\frac{\pi}{2})1 \\ (-\sin\frac{\pi}{2})0 + (\cos\frac{\pi}{2})1 \end{bmatrix} = \begin{bmatrix} -1 \\ 0 \end{bmatrix} \tag{5.34}$$

This has transformed the state from $|1\rangle$ to $-|0\rangle$

5.3.2 RY Gate

The RY gate is a gate that does a rotation around the Y-axis by a specified amount which is normally denoted by θ.

$$RY = \begin{bmatrix} \cos\frac{\theta}{2} & -\sin\frac{\theta}{2} \\ \sin\frac{\theta}{2} & \cos\frac{\theta}{2} \end{bmatrix} \tag{5.35}$$

Using the matrix multiplication we can see how the RY gate operates on the qubits state. For our first example lets initialise the qubits state to $|0\rangle$ and set θ to be π. This should flip the qubits state from $|0\rangle$ to $|1\rangle$:

$$\begin{bmatrix} \cos\frac{\pi}{2} & -\sin\frac{\pi}{2} \\ \sin\frac{\pi}{2} & \cos\frac{\pi}{2} \end{bmatrix} \begin{bmatrix} 1 \\ 0 \end{bmatrix} = \begin{bmatrix} (\cos\frac{\pi}{2})1 + (-\sin\frac{\pi}{2})0 \\ (\sin\frac{\pi}{2})1 + (\cos\frac{\pi}{2})0 \end{bmatrix} = \begin{bmatrix} 0 \\ 1 \end{bmatrix} \tag{5.36}$$

Which is correct as the column vector $\begin{bmatrix} 0 \\ 1 \end{bmatrix} = |1\rangle$

If we initialise the qubit to $|1\rangle$:

$$\begin{bmatrix} \cos\frac{\pi}{2} & -\sin\frac{\pi}{2} \\ \sin\frac{\pi}{2} & \cos\frac{\pi}{2} \end{bmatrix} \begin{bmatrix} 0 \\ 1 \end{bmatrix} = \begin{bmatrix} (\cos\frac{\pi}{2})0 + (-\sin\frac{\pi}{2})1 \\ (\sin\frac{\pi}{2})0 + (\cos\frac{\pi}{2})1 \end{bmatrix} = \begin{bmatrix} -1 \\ 0 \end{bmatrix} \tag{5.37}$$

Which has changed the qubits state from $|1\rangle$ to $-|0\rangle$

5.3.3 RZ Gate

The RZ gate is a gate that does a rotation around the Z-axis The amount of rotations are normally denoted by λ for the Z-axis.

$$RZ = \begin{bmatrix} e^{-i\frac{\lambda}{2}} & 0 \\ 0 & e^{i\frac{\lambda}{2}} \end{bmatrix} \tag{5.38}$$

In our first example lets initialise the qubit to $|0\rangle$ and set λ to π:

$$\begin{bmatrix} e^{-i\frac{\pi}{2}} & 0 \\ 0 & e^{i\frac{\pi}{2}} \end{bmatrix} \begin{bmatrix} 1 \\ 0 \end{bmatrix} = \begin{bmatrix} (e^{-i\frac{\pi}{2}})1 + (0)0 \\ (0)1 + (e^{i\frac{\pi}{2}})0 \end{bmatrix} = \begin{bmatrix} -i \\ 0 \end{bmatrix} \tag{5.39}$$

Which mean the qubit has changed from $|0\rangle$ to $-i|0\rangle$

Now lets see what happens when we set the qubit to $|1\rangle$ and set λ to π:

$$\begin{bmatrix} e^{-i\frac{\pi}{2}} & 0 \\ 0 & e^{i\frac{\pi}{2}} \end{bmatrix} \begin{bmatrix} 0 \\ 1 \end{bmatrix} = \begin{bmatrix} (e^{-i\frac{\pi}{2}})0 + (0)1 \\ (0)0 + (e^{i\frac{\pi}{2}})1 \end{bmatrix} = \begin{bmatrix} 0 \\ i \end{bmatrix} \tag{5.40}$$

Which has the qubits state from $|1\rangle$ to $i|1\rangle$

5.3.4 U1 Gate

The U1 gate is a single rotation gate that does a rotation around the Z axis by λ. It is represented by the following matrix:

$$U1 = \begin{bmatrix} 1 & 0 \\ 0 & e^{i\lambda} \end{bmatrix} \tag{5.41}$$

For our first example lets set the qubits state to $|0\rangle$ and λ by π:

$$\begin{bmatrix} 1 & 0 \\ 0 & e^{i\pi} \end{bmatrix} \begin{bmatrix} 1 \\ 0 \end{bmatrix} = \begin{bmatrix} (1)1 + (0)0 \\ (0)1 + (e^{i\pi})0 \end{bmatrix} = \begin{bmatrix} 1 \\ 0 \end{bmatrix} \tag{5.42}$$

Which much like the Z gate has left the qubits state unchanged.

Now lets set the qubit to $|1\rangle$ and leave λ as π:

$$\begin{bmatrix} 1 & 0 \\ 0 & e^{i\pi} \end{bmatrix} \begin{bmatrix} 0 \\ 1 \end{bmatrix} = \begin{bmatrix} (1)0 + (0)1 \\ (0)0 + (e^{i\pi})1 \end{bmatrix} = \begin{bmatrix} 0 \\ -1 \end{bmatrix} \tag{5.43}$$

Which has changed the qubits state from $|0\rangle$ to $-|1\rangle$

5.3.5 U2 Gate

The U2 gate is a single rotation gate that does a rotation around the X and Z axis by λ and ϕ. It is represented by the following matrix:

$$U2(\phi\lambda) = \frac{1}{\sqrt{2}} \begin{bmatrix} 1 & -e^{i\lambda} \\ e^{i\phi} & e^{i(\phi+\lambda)} \end{bmatrix} \tag{5.44}$$

In order to see how the U2 gate operates on an qubit lets use some examples. For our first example we will implement an RX gate that rotates by $\frac{\pi}{2}$ by setting ϕ to $-\frac{\pi}{2}$ and λ to $\frac{\pi}{2}$. The qubit state will be initialised to $|0\rangle$ and the associated column vector to $\begin{bmatrix} 1 \\ 0 \end{bmatrix}$

$$\frac{1}{\sqrt{2}} \begin{bmatrix} 1 & -e^{i\frac{\pi}{2}} \\ e^{i-\frac{\pi}{2}} & e^{i(-\frac{\pi}{2}+\frac{\pi}{2})} \end{bmatrix} \begin{bmatrix} 1 \\ 0 \end{bmatrix} = \begin{bmatrix} (1)1 + (-e^{i\frac{\pi}{2}})0 \\ (e^{i-\frac{\pi}{2}})1 + (e^{i(-\frac{\pi}{2}+\frac{\pi}{2})})0 \end{bmatrix} = \frac{1}{\sqrt{2}} \begin{bmatrix} 1 \\ -i \end{bmatrix}$$

$$\tag{5.45}$$

$\begin{bmatrix} 1 \\ -i \end{bmatrix}$ means that the qubits state is in a superposition of $|0\rangle$ and $-i|1\rangle$. This is correct as the same would happen with a RX gate that rotates around the axis with an angle of $\frac{\pi}{2}$.

If we apply another U2 gate using the same parameters the qubits state should flip to $-i|1\rangle$.

$$\frac{1}{\sqrt{2}}\begin{bmatrix} 1 & -e^{i\frac{pi}{2}} \\ e^{i-\frac{pi}{2}} & e^{i(-\frac{pi}{2}+\frac{pi}{2})} \end{bmatrix}\begin{bmatrix} 1 \\ -i \end{bmatrix} = \begin{bmatrix} (1)1+(-e^{i\frac{\pi}{2}})-i \\ (e^{i-\frac{\pi}{2}})1+(e^{i(-\frac{\pi}{2}+\frac{\pi}{2})})-i \end{bmatrix} = \begin{bmatrix} 0 \\ -i \end{bmatrix}$$

$$(5.46)$$

Which is correct as $\begin{bmatrix} 0 \\ -i \end{bmatrix}$ is the associated column vector for $-i|1\rangle$.

5.3.6 U3 Gate

A U3 gate is a gate that does a rotation around the bloch sphere with 3 angles. The three angles used to perform the rotations are θ, λ, and ϕ. The U3 gate is the most common of these rotation gates as it can be used to rotate around any axis and is a universal single quantum gate.

The matrix for the U3 gate is:

$$U3 = \begin{bmatrix} \cos(\frac{\theta}{2}) & -e^{i\lambda}\sin(\frac{\theta}{2}) \\ e^{i\phi}\sin(\frac{\theta}{2}) & e^{i(\phi+\lambda)}\cos(\frac{\theta}{2}) \end{bmatrix}$$

$$(5.47)$$

The U3 gate can replicate any other gate.For example to replicate the Pauli-X gate you would rotate θ by π, ϕ by π and λ by $\frac{\pi}{2}$:

$$U3(\pi,\pi,\frac{\pi}{2}) = X$$

$$(5.48)$$

Where $U3(\pi,\pi,\frac{\pi}{2}) = U3(\theta,\phi,\lambda)$

As an example lets replicate a Pauli-X gate and set the qubit state to $|1\rangle$. To see how the U3 gate operates on the qubit we multiply the column vector associated with $|1\rangle$ by the U3 matrix.

$$\begin{bmatrix} \cos(\frac{\pi}{2}) & -e^{i\pi}\sin(\frac{\pi}{2}) \\ e^{i\pi}\sin(\frac{\pi}{2}) & e^{i(\pi+\frac{\pi}{2})}\cos(\frac{\pi}{2}) \end{bmatrix} \begin{bmatrix} 0 \\ 1 \end{bmatrix} = \tag{5.49}$$

$$\begin{bmatrix} (\cos(\frac{\pi}{2}))0 + (-e^{i\frac{\pi}{2}}\sin(\frac{\pi}{2}))1 \\ (e^{i\pi}\sin(\frac{\pi}{2}))0 + (e^{i(\pi+\frac{\pi}{2})}\cos(\frac{\pi}{2}))1 \end{bmatrix} = \begin{bmatrix} (-1)0 + (1)1 \\ (-1)0 + (0)1 \end{bmatrix} = \begin{bmatrix} 1 \\ 0 \end{bmatrix}$$
$$\tag{5.50}$$

This is correct as the resulting column vector $\begin{pmatrix} 1 \\ 0 \end{pmatrix}$ is the column vector for $|0\rangle$. This shows that the qubits state has flipped from $|1\rangle$ to $|0\rangle$.

If we wanted to use a U3 gate to create a Hadamard gate then it would be:

$$U3(\frac{\pi}{2}, 0, \pi) \tag{5.51}$$

Let's prove this by setting the qubit to $|0\rangle$ and multiply the state vector by the U3 gate with the parameters set as the equation above:

$$\begin{bmatrix} \cos(\frac{\pi/2}{2}) & -e^{i\pi}\sin(\frac{\pi/2}{2}) \\ e^{i0}\sin(\frac{\pi/2}{2}) & e^{i(0+\pi)}\cos(\frac{\pi/2}{2}) \end{bmatrix} \begin{bmatrix} 1 \\ 0 \end{bmatrix} \tag{5.52}$$

$$= \begin{bmatrix} (\cos(\frac{\pi/2}{2})(1)) + (-e^{i\pi}\sin(\frac{\pi/2}{2})(0)) \\ (e^{i0}\sin(\frac{\pi/2}{2})(1)) + (e^{i(0+\pi)}\cos(\frac{\pi/2}{2})(0)) \end{bmatrix} = \frac{1}{\sqrt{2}}\begin{bmatrix} 1 \\ 1 \end{bmatrix} \tag{5.53}$$

Which has put the qubit in to superposition just as the Hadamard gate would!

5.4 Multi-qubit gates

The gates that we have described above are single qubit gates meaning that they only act on a single qubit by rotating its state via a specific angle or axis or perhaps a mixture. However another set of gates allow you to change the state of a qubit based on the state of another. These are called multi-qubit gates and are very important in quantum computing.

5.4.1 CNOT Gate

The most simple but most important multi-qubit gate is the Controlled NOT gate or CNOT gate for short. This is a two qubit gate consisting of a control qubit and a target qubit. If the control qubits state is $|1\rangle$ then the state of the target qubit will be flipped from $|0\rangle$ to $|1\rangle$ or vice versa.

This gate is also known as a universal quantum gate as any quantum algorithm can be implemented using CNOT gates alone.

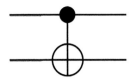

Figure 5.5: Circuit diagram of a CNOT gate

$$CNOT = \begin{bmatrix} 1 & 0 & 0 & 0 \\ 0 & 1 & 0 & 0 \\ 0 & 0 & 0 & 1 \\ 0 & 0 & 1 & 0 \end{bmatrix} \quad (5.54)$$

Using matrix multiplication let's explore how the CNOT gate operates on the qubits state. Since this gate operates on two qubits the column vectors will have a row for each possible state:

$$|00\rangle = \begin{bmatrix} 1 \\ 0 \\ 0 \\ 0 \end{bmatrix} |01\rangle = \begin{bmatrix} 0 \\ 1 \\ 0 \\ 0 \end{bmatrix} |10\rangle = \begin{bmatrix} 0 \\ 0 \\ 1 \\ 0 \end{bmatrix} |11\rangle = \begin{bmatrix} 0 \\ 0 \\ 0 \\ 1 \end{bmatrix} \quad (5.55)$$

For our first example let's set the control qubit and target qubit to $|0\rangle$ such that the combined state will be $|00\rangle = \begin{bmatrix} 1 \\ 0 \\ 0 \\ 0 \end{bmatrix}$

$$\begin{bmatrix} 1 & 0 & 0 & 0 \\ 0 & 1 & 0 & 0 \\ 0 & 0 & 0 & 1 \\ 0 & 0 & 1 & 0 \end{bmatrix} \begin{bmatrix} 1 \\ 0 \\ 0 \\ 0 \end{bmatrix} = \begin{bmatrix} 1(1)+0(0)+0(0)+0(0) \\ 0(1)+1(0)+0(0)+0(0) \\ 0(1)+0(0)+0(0)+1(0) \\ 0(1)+0(0)+1(0)+0(0) \end{bmatrix} = \begin{bmatrix} 1 \\ 0 \\ 0 \\ 0 \end{bmatrix}$$
(5.56)

This shows that the target qubits state has remained unchanged as the state is $|00\rangle$

Now let's instead set the control qubit to $|1\rangle$ and the target qubit to $|0\rangle$ such that the combined state will be $|10\rangle$:

$$\begin{bmatrix} 1 & 0 & 0 & 0 \\ 0 & 1 & 0 & 0 \\ 0 & 0 & 0 & 1 \\ 0 & 0 & 1 & 0 \end{bmatrix} \begin{bmatrix} 0 \\ 0 \\ 1 \\ 0 \end{bmatrix} = \begin{bmatrix} 1(0) + 0(0) + 0(1) + 0(0) \\ 0(0) + 1(0) + 0(1) + 0(0) \\ 0(0) + 0(0) + 0(1) + 1(0) \\ 0(0) + 0(0) + 1(1) + 0(0) \end{bmatrix} = \begin{bmatrix} 0 \\ 0 \\ 0 \\ 1 \end{bmatrix}$$

$$(5.57)$$

Which has flipped the target qubit to $|1\rangle$ such that the combined state is $|11\rangle$

Now if we set both the control and target qubit to $|1\rangle$ such that the combined state will be $|11\rangle$:

$$\begin{bmatrix} 1 & 0 & 0 & 0 \\ 0 & 1 & 0 & 0 \\ 0 & 0 & 0 & 1 \\ 0 & 0 & 1 & 0 \end{bmatrix} \begin{bmatrix} 0 \\ 0 \\ 0 \\ 1 \end{bmatrix} = \begin{bmatrix} 1(0) + 0(0) + 0(0) + 0(1) \\ 0(0) + 1(0) + 0(0) + 0(1) \\ 0(0) + 0(0) + 0(0) + 1(1) \\ 0(0) + 0(0) + 1(0) + 0(1) \end{bmatrix} = \begin{bmatrix} 0 \\ 0 \\ 1 \\ 0 \end{bmatrix}$$

$$(5.58)$$

Which has flipped the target qubit from $|1\rangle$ to $|0\rangle$ therefore flipping the combined state from $|11\rangle$ to $|10\rangle$.

5.4.2 Toffoli Gate

The Toffoli gate is a 3 qubit gate that is like the CNOT gate but instead has two control qubits. Simply put if both control qubits are $|1\rangle$ then target qubits state will be flipped.

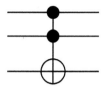

Figure 5.6: Circuit diagram of a Toffoli gate

$$Toffoli = \begin{bmatrix} 1 & 0 & 0 & 0 & 0 & 0 & 0 & 0 \\ 0 & 1 & 0 & 0 & 0 & 0 & 0 & 0 \\ 0 & 0 & 1 & 0 & 0 & 0 & 0 & 0 \\ 0 & 0 & 0 & 1 & 0 & 0 & 0 & 0 \\ 0 & 0 & 0 & 0 & 1 & 0 & 0 & 0 \\ 0 & 0 & 0 & 0 & 0 & 1 & 0 & 0 \\ 0 & 0 & 0 & 0 & 0 & 0 & 0 & 1 \\ 0 & 0 & 0 & 0 & 0 & 0 & 1 & 0 \end{bmatrix} \tag{5.59}$$

As stated in the section on CNOT gates when dealing with multiple qubit gates the column vector will include a row for every possible state. Since the Toffoli gate is a 3 qubit gate the column vectors will contain 8 rows corresponding to each state.

$$|000\rangle = \begin{bmatrix} 1 \\ 0 \\ 0 \\ 0 \\ 0 \\ 0 \\ 0 \\ 0 \end{bmatrix} \quad |001\rangle = \begin{bmatrix} 0 \\ 1 \\ 0 \\ 0 \\ 0 \\ 0 \\ 0 \\ 0 \end{bmatrix} \quad |010\rangle = \begin{bmatrix} 0 \\ 0 \\ 1 \\ 0 \\ 0 \\ 0 \\ 0 \\ 0 \end{bmatrix} \quad |011\rangle = \begin{bmatrix} 0 \\ 0 \\ 0 \\ 1 \\ 0 \\ 0 \\ 0 \\ 0 \end{bmatrix} \cdots |111\rangle = \begin{bmatrix} 0 \\ 0 \\ 0 \\ 0 \\ 0 \\ 0 \\ 0 \\ 1 \end{bmatrix} \tag{5.60}$$

Using matrix multiplication lets see why the Toffoli gate flips the target qubit if both control qubits are $|1\rangle$ such that combined

$$\text{state will be } |110\rangle = \begin{bmatrix} 0 \\ 0 \\ 0 \\ 0 \\ 0 \\ 0 \\ 1 \\ 0 \end{bmatrix}$$

$$\begin{bmatrix} 1 & 0 & 0 & 0 & 0 & 0 & 0 & 0 \\ 0 & 1 & 0 & 0 & 0 & 0 & 0 & 0 \\ 0 & 0 & 1 & 0 & 0 & 0 & 0 & 0 \\ 0 & 0 & 0 & 1 & 0 & 0 & 0 & 0 \\ 0 & 0 & 0 & 0 & 1 & 0 & 0 & 0 \\ 0 & 0 & 0 & 0 & 0 & 1 & 0 & 0 \\ 0 & 0 & 0 & 0 & 0 & 0 & 0 & 1 \\ 0 & 0 & 0 & 0 & 0 & 0 & 1 & 0 \end{bmatrix} \begin{bmatrix} 0 \\ 0 \\ 0 \\ 0 \\ 0 \\ 0 \\ 1 \\ 0 \end{bmatrix} \quad (5.61)$$

$$= \begin{bmatrix} 1(0) & 0(0) & 0(0) & 0(0) & 0(0) & 0(0) & 0(1) & 0(0) \\ 0(0) & 1(0) & 0(0) & 0(0) & 0(0) & 0(0) & 0(1) & 0(0) \\ 0(0) & 0(0) & 1(0) & 0(0) & 0(0) & 0(0) & 0(1) & 0(0) \\ 0(0) & 0(0) & 0(0) & 1(0) & 0(0) & 0(0) & 0(1) & 0(0) \\ 0(0) & 0(0) & 0(0) & 0(0) & 1(0) & 0(0) & 0(1) & 0(0) \\ 0(0) & 0(0) & 0(0) & 0(0) & 0(0) & 1(0) & 0(1) & 0(0) \\ 0(0) & 0(0) & 0(0) & 0(0) & 0(0) & 0(0) & 0(1) & 1(0) \\ 0(0) & 0(0) & 0(0) & 0(0) & 0(0) & 0(0) & 1(1) & 0(0) \end{bmatrix} = \begin{bmatrix} 0 \\ 0 \\ 0 \\ 0 \\ 0 \\ 0 \\ 0 \\ 1 \end{bmatrix}$$

$$(5.62)$$

This has flipped the target qubit from $|0\rangle$ to $|1\rangle$ such that combined state has flipped from $|110\rangle$ to $|111\rangle$

5.4.3 CNOT Gate with N control qubits

With the CNOT gate we can see that it uses 1 control qubit and the Toffoli gate uses 2 control qubits. However how can we create a CNOT gate that consists of N control qubits? One way is by chaining Toffoli gates like in the figure below which uses Toffoli gates to create a CNOT gate consisting of 4 control qubits and 1 target qubit.

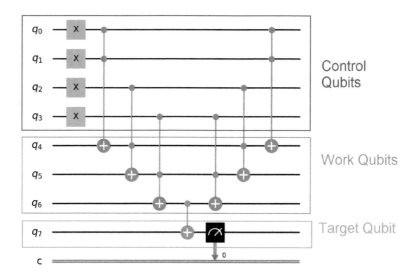

Figure 5.7: CNOT gate with 4 control qubits.

5.4.4 Swap Gate

The swap gate is a two qubit gate that swaps the states of two qubits. For example given two qubits q_0 and q_1 lets say q_0 is $|1\rangle$ and q_1 is $|0\rangle$ the swap gate will swap the states such that q_0 will now be $|0\rangle$ and q_1 will be $|1\rangle$.

$$SWAP = \begin{bmatrix} 1 & 0 & 0 & 0 \\ 0 & 0 & 1 & 0 \\ 0 & 1 & 0 & 0 \\ 0 & 0 & 0 & 1 \end{bmatrix} \tag{5.63}$$

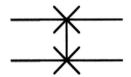

Figure 5.8: Circuit diagram of a Swap gate

For our example let's set the first qubit to $|1\rangle$ and the second qubit to $|0\rangle$ and apply a swap gate. For this the input column vector will be:

$$|10\rangle = \begin{bmatrix} 0 \\ 0 \\ 1 \\ 0 \end{bmatrix} \tag{5.64}$$

$$\begin{bmatrix} 1 & 0 & 0 & 0 \\ 0 & 0 & 1 & 0 \\ 0 & 1 & 0 & 0 \\ 0 & 0 & 0 & 1 \end{bmatrix} \begin{bmatrix} 0 \\ 0 \\ 1 \\ 0 \end{bmatrix} = \begin{bmatrix} 1(0) & 0(0) & 0(1) & 0(0) \\ 0(0) & 0(0) & 1(1) & 0(0) \\ 0(0) & 1(0) & 0(1) & 0(0) \\ 0(0) & 0(0) & 0(1) & 1(0) \end{bmatrix} = \begin{bmatrix} 0 \\ 1 \\ 0 \\ 0 \end{bmatrix} \tag{5.65}$$

5 Quantum logic gates

Which has swapped the state between qubit 1 and 2 such that qubit 1 is now $|0\rangle$ and the qubit 2 is $|1\rangle$. This corresponds to the combined state $|01\rangle$. With the swap gate we have seen how it swaps states when the qubits are initialised in the computational basis (ie $|0\rangle$ and $|1\rangle$)). However it is possible to swap a superposition of states.

For our example let's initialise the first qubit to $|0\rangle$ and then apply a Hadamard gate to put it in to superpositon:

$$\frac{1}{\sqrt{2}}\begin{bmatrix} 1 & 1 \\ 1 & -1 \end{bmatrix}\begin{bmatrix} 1 \\ 0 \end{bmatrix} = \frac{1}{\sqrt{2}}\begin{bmatrix} 1(1)+1(0) \\ 1(1)+-1(0) \end{bmatrix} = \frac{1}{\sqrt{2}}\begin{bmatrix} 1 \\ 1 \end{bmatrix} \quad (5.66)$$

Since the first qubit is in superposition the combined state will look like this:

$$\frac{1}{\sqrt{2}}\begin{bmatrix} 1 \\ 0 \\ 1 \\ 0 \end{bmatrix} \quad (5.67)$$

Now let's apply the Swap gate:

$$\begin{bmatrix} 1 & 0 & 0 & 0 \\ 0 & 0 & 1 & 0 \\ 0 & 1 & 0 & 0 \\ 0 & 0 & 0 & 1 \end{bmatrix}\frac{1}{\sqrt{2}}\begin{bmatrix} 1 \\ 0 \\ 1 \\ 0 \end{bmatrix} = \frac{1}{\sqrt{2}}\begin{bmatrix} 1(1)+0(0)+0(1)+0(0) \\ 0(1)+0(0)+1(1)+0(0) \\ 0(1)+1(0)+0(1)+0(0) \\ 0(1)+0(0)+0(1)+1(0) \end{bmatrix} = \frac{1}{\sqrt{2}}\begin{bmatrix} 1 \\ 1 \\ 0 \\ 0 \end{bmatrix}$$
$$(5.68)$$

This has swapped the qubits states from $\frac{|00\rangle+|10\rangle}{\sqrt{2}}$ to $\frac{|00\rangle+|01\rangle}{\sqrt{2}}$

5.4.5 Fredkin Gate

The Fredkin gate (also called the CSWAP gate) is a controlled swap gate consisting of 3 qubits. The first qubit is the control qubit and the other two are the qubits whose states we wish to swap. If the state of the control qubit is $|1\rangle$ then the states of the two qubits will be swapped.

For example lets say we have 3 qubits t_0, q_0, and q_1. If t_0 is $|0\rangle$ then the states of q_0 and q_0 will be unchanged. However if t_0 is $|1\rangle$ then the states will be swapped.

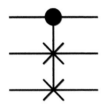

Figure 5.9: Circuit diagram of a Fredkin gate

The operation of the Fredkin gate is described by the following matrix:

$$
Fredkin =
\begin{bmatrix}
1 & 0 & 0 & 0 & 0 & 0 & 0 & 0 \\
0 & 1 & 0 & 0 & 0 & 0 & 0 & 0 \\
0 & 0 & 1 & 0 & 0 & 0 & 0 & 0 \\
0 & 0 & 0 & 1 & 0 & 0 & 0 & 0 \\
0 & 0 & 0 & 0 & 1 & 0 & 0 & 0 \\
0 & 0 & 0 & 0 & 0 & 0 & 1 & 0 \\
0 & 0 & 0 & 0 & 0 & 1 & 0 & 0 \\
0 & 0 & 0 & 0 & 0 & 0 & 0 & 1
\end{bmatrix}
\tag{5.69}
$$

Using matrix multiplication we can see how the Fredkin gate operates on a qubits state. For our first example let's set all qubits to $|0\rangle$ and multiply the combined state by the Fredkin gates matrix:

$$
\begin{bmatrix}
1 & 0 & 0 & 0 & 0 & 0 & 0 & 0 \\
0 & 1 & 0 & 0 & 0 & 0 & 0 & 0 \\
0 & 0 & 1 & 0 & 0 & 0 & 0 & 0 \\
0 & 0 & 0 & 1 & 0 & 0 & 0 & 0 \\
0 & 0 & 0 & 0 & 1 & 0 & 0 & 0 \\
0 & 0 & 0 & 0 & 0 & 0 & 1 & 0 \\
0 & 0 & 0 & 0 & 0 & 1 & 0 & 0 \\
0 & 0 & 0 & 0 & 0 & 0 & 0 & 1
\end{bmatrix}
\begin{bmatrix}
1 \\ 0 \\ 0 \\ 0 \\ 0 \\ 0 \\ 0 \\ 0
\end{bmatrix}
=
\begin{bmatrix}
1 \\ 0 \\ 0 \\ 0 \\ 0 \\ 0 \\ 0 \\ 0
\end{bmatrix}
\tag{5.70}
$$

Which has not affected the qubits states.

For our second example let's set the control qubit to $|1\rangle$ and the second and third qubit to $|1\rangle$ and $|0\rangle$ respectively. This should swap the seconds qubits state with the third qubits state.

$$
\begin{bmatrix}
1 & 0 & 0 & 0 & 0 & 0 & 0 & 0 \\
0 & 1 & 0 & 0 & 0 & 0 & 0 & 0 \\
0 & 0 & 1 & 0 & 0 & 0 & 0 & 0 \\
0 & 0 & 0 & 1 & 0 & 0 & 0 & 0 \\
0 & 0 & 0 & 0 & 1 & 0 & 0 & 0 \\
0 & 0 & 0 & 0 & 0 & 0 & 1 & 0 \\
0 & 0 & 0 & 0 & 0 & 1 & 0 & 0 \\
0 & 0 & 0 & 0 & 0 & 0 & 0 & 1
\end{bmatrix}
\begin{bmatrix}
0 \\ 0 \\ 0 \\ 0 \\ 0 \\ 1 \\ 0 \\ 0
\end{bmatrix}
\tag{5.71}
$$

$$
= \begin{bmatrix}
1(0) + 0(0) + 0(0) + 0(1) + 0(0) + 0(1) + 0(0) + 0(0) \\
0(0) + 1(0) + 0(0) + 0(1) + 0(0) + 0(1) + 0(0) + 0(0) \\
0(0) + 0(0) + 1(0) + 0(1) + 0(0) + 0(1) + 0(0) + 0(0) \\
0(0) + 0(0) + 0(0) + 1(1) + 0(0) + 0(1) + 0(0) + 0(0) \\
0(0) + 0(0) + 0(0) + 0(1) + 1(0) + 0(1) + 0(0) + 0(0) \\
0(0) + 0(0) + 0(0) + 0(1) + 0(0) + 0(1) + 1(0) + 0(0) \\
0(0) + 0(0) + 0(0) + 0(1) + 0(0) + 1(1) + 0(0) + 0(0) \\
0(0) + 0(0) + 0(0) + 0(1) + 1(0) + 0(1) + 0(0) + 1(0)
\end{bmatrix}
= \begin{bmatrix}
0 \\ 0 \\ 0 \\ 0 \\ 0 \\ 0 \\ 1 \\ 0
\end{bmatrix}
$$

$$(5.72)$$

Which has swapped the states of the second and third qubits. As such the combined state has changed from $|110\rangle$ to $|101\rangle$

5.4.6 Controlled Hadamard Gate

A controlled Hadamard gate is a controlled gate consisting of two qubits. When the control qubit is $|1\rangle$ it will apply a Hadamard gate to the target qubit.

The matrix for the Controlled Hadamard gate is:

$$
CH = \begin{bmatrix}
1 & 0 & 0 & 0 \\
0 & \frac{1}{\sqrt{2}} & 0 & \frac{1}{\sqrt{2}} \\
0 & 0 & 1 & 0 \\
0 & \frac{1}{\sqrt{2}} & 0 & -\frac{1}{\sqrt{2}}
\end{bmatrix}
$$

$$(5.73)$$

As with the other gates explained earlier we can multiply the column vector by the controlled Hadamard gates matrix. For our first example lets initialise both qubits to $|0\rangle$. For this the associated column vector will be:

$$|00\rangle = \begin{bmatrix} 1 \\ 0 \\ 0 \\ 0 \end{bmatrix} \qquad (5.74)$$

$$\begin{bmatrix} 1 & 0 & 0 & 0 \\ 0 & \frac{1}{\sqrt{2}} & 0 & \frac{1}{\sqrt{2}} \\ 0 & 0 & 1 & 0 \\ 0 & \frac{1}{\sqrt{2}} & 0 & -\frac{1}{\sqrt{2}} \end{bmatrix} \begin{bmatrix} 1 \\ 0 \\ 0 \\ 0 \end{bmatrix} = \begin{bmatrix} 1(1) + 0(0) + 0(0) + 0(0) \\ 0(1) + \frac{1}{\sqrt{2}}(0) + 0(0) + \frac{1}{\sqrt{2}}(0) \\ 0(1) + 0(0) + 1(0) + 0(0) \\ 0(1) + \frac{1}{\sqrt{2}}(0) + 0(0) + -\frac{1}{\sqrt{2}}(0) \end{bmatrix} = \begin{bmatrix} 1 \\ 0 \\ 0 \\ 0 \end{bmatrix}$$

$$(5.75)$$

Which has left out state unchanged as the control qubit was $|0\rangle$. For our next example we will set the control qubit to $|1\rangle$ and the target qubit to $|0\rangle$.

As a column vector this would be: $\begin{bmatrix} 0 \\ 1 \\ 0 \\ 0 \end{bmatrix}$

$$\begin{bmatrix} 1 & 0 & 0 & 0 \\ 0 & \frac{1}{\sqrt{2}} & 0 & \frac{1}{\sqrt{2}} \\ 0 & 0 & 1 & 0 \\ 0 & \frac{1}{\sqrt{2}} & 0 & -\frac{1}{\sqrt{2}} \end{bmatrix} \begin{bmatrix} 0 \\ 1 \\ 0 \\ 0 \end{bmatrix} = \begin{bmatrix} 1(0) + 0(1) + 0(0) + 0(0) \\ 0(0) + \frac{1}{\sqrt{2}}(1) + 0(0) + \frac{1}{\sqrt{2}}(0) \\ 0(0) + 0(1) + 1(0) + 0(0) \\ 0(0) + \frac{1}{\sqrt{2}}(1) + 0(0) + -\frac{1}{\sqrt{2}}(0) \end{bmatrix} = \frac{1}{\sqrt{2}} \begin{bmatrix} 0 \\ 1 \\ 0 \\ 1 \end{bmatrix}$$

$$(5.76)$$

This means that the Hadamard gate has put the system in to a superposition of $|01\rangle$ and $|11\rangle$. Like with the single qubit Hadamard gate the controlled described here is actually reversible and conforms to the identity HH=I meaning that if two controlled Hadamard gates are applied we will get back the previous state.

Let's apply another controlled Hadamard gate by multiplying the resulting column vector in eq 6.54 with the controlled Hadamard gate matrix:

$$\begin{bmatrix} 1 & 0 & 0 & 0 \\ 0 & \frac{1}{\sqrt{2}} & 0 & \frac{1}{\sqrt{2}} \\ 0 & 0 & 1 & 0 \\ 0 & \frac{1}{\sqrt{2}} & 0 & -\frac{1}{\sqrt{2}} \end{bmatrix} \frac{1}{\sqrt{2}} \begin{bmatrix} 0 \\ 1 \\ 0 \\ 1 \end{bmatrix} \tag{5.77}$$

$$= \frac{1}{\sqrt{2}} \begin{bmatrix} 1(0) + 0(1) + 0(0) + 0(1) \\ 0(0) + \frac{1}{\sqrt{2}}(1) + 0(0) + \frac{1}{\sqrt{2}}(1) \\ 0(0) + 0(1) + 1(0) + 0(1) \\ 0(0) + \frac{1}{\sqrt{2}}(1) + 0(0) + -\frac{1}{\sqrt{2}}(1) \end{bmatrix} = \frac{1}{\sqrt{2}} \frac{1}{\sqrt{2}} \begin{bmatrix} 0 \\ 2 \\ 0 \\ 0 \end{bmatrix} = \begin{bmatrix} 0 \\ 1 \\ 0 \\ 0 \end{bmatrix}$$

$$\tag{5.78}$$

6 Quantum Circuits

In gate based quantum computing logic gates can be combined together to create quantum circuits. In order to visualize a quantum circuit we can use a diagram called a circuit diagram. The term circuit can be misleading as quantum circuits are not the actual physical circuits found in the quantum hardware. Instead it is best to think of quantum circuits as a sequence of operations (using logic gates) applied to qubits. In this chapter we will go through various examples of quantum circuits including the all important bell circuit.

6.1 HZH Circuit

Let's start with a very simple example called the HZH circuit. This is a 1 qubit circuit where a Hadamard gate is applied followed by a Z gate and a closing Hadamard gate.

Figure 6.1: Circuit diagram of the HZH circuit

67

Like with the single and multiple qubit gates we can use matrix multiplication to analyse how each logic gate will affect the qubits state. In the circuit the qubit is first initialised to $|0\rangle$ such that its column vector will be:

$$|0\rangle = \begin{bmatrix} 1 \\ 0 \end{bmatrix} \tag{6.1}$$

With a single qubit circuit all we have to do is multiply the column vector by the matrix of each logic gate in the circuit. The first gate applied is the Hadamard gate so we first apply that:

$$\frac{1}{\sqrt{2}} \begin{bmatrix} 1 & 1 \\ 1 & -1 \end{bmatrix} \begin{bmatrix} 1 \\ 0 \end{bmatrix} = \frac{1}{\sqrt{2}} \begin{bmatrix} 1(1) + 1(0) \\ 1(1) + -1(0) \end{bmatrix} = \frac{1}{\sqrt{2}} \begin{bmatrix} 1 \\ 1 \end{bmatrix} \tag{6.2}$$

Next we apply the Z gate:

$$\begin{bmatrix} 1 & 0 \\ 0 & -1 \end{bmatrix} \frac{1}{\sqrt{2}} \begin{bmatrix} 1 \\ 1 \end{bmatrix} = \frac{1}{\sqrt{2}} \begin{bmatrix} 1(1) + 0(1) \\ 0(0) + -1(1) \end{bmatrix} = \frac{1}{\sqrt{2}} \begin{bmatrix} 1 \\ -1 \end{bmatrix} \tag{6.3}$$

And finally we apply the closing Hadamard gate:

$$\frac{1}{\sqrt{2}} \begin{bmatrix} 1 & 1 \\ 1 & -1 \end{bmatrix} \frac{1}{\sqrt{2}} \begin{bmatrix} 1 \\ -1 \end{bmatrix} = \left(\frac{1}{\sqrt{2}} \begin{bmatrix} 1(1) + 1(-1) \\ 1(1) + -1(-1) \end{bmatrix} \right)^2 = \begin{bmatrix} 0 \\ 1 \end{bmatrix} \tag{6.4}$$

Where the resulting column vector = $|1\rangle$. As such we have shown that the HZH circuit can flip the qubit from $|0\rangle$ to $|1\rangle$ by flipping the phase using a Z gate while the qubit is in superposition.

6.2 Bell Circuit

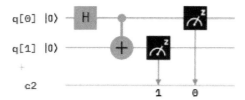

Figure 6.2: Circuit diagram of a bell circuit

The diagram above is a quantum circuit that prepares a Bell pair. This is the simplest circuit that can be used to entangle two qubits such that the combined state becomes:

$$\frac{|00\rangle + |11\rangle}{\sqrt{2}} \tag{6.5}$$

As you can see it consists of 2 qubits denoted as q_0 and q_1. First q_0 and q_1 are initialized to the state $|0\rangle$. Next a Hadamard gate is applied to q_0 and a CNOT gate applied to q_1 where q_0 is the control qubit. After this both qubits are measured. If q_0 is $|1\rangle$ then it will flip q_1 to $|1\rangle$ such that state of the quantum system will be $|11\rangle$ Otherwise if q_0 is $|0\rangle$ then both qubits will be unchanged such that the system state will be $|00\rangle$.

A quantum circuit can have as many qubits and logic gates as needed. The quantity of logic gates in a row is known as the depth of the circuit. When designing quantum circuits it is best to use the lowest amount of qubits and logic gates possible.

Up to this point I have only shown how matrices work for single and multiple qubit gates. However it is very beneficial to see how matrices can be used to describe entire circuits. As such we will go through step by step how to describe the Bell circuit using matrices. Since the b=Bell circuit consists of two qubits both initialised to $|0\rangle$ the initial combined state will be:

$$|00\rangle = \begin{bmatrix} 1 \\ 0 \\ 0 \\ 0 \end{bmatrix} \tag{6.6}$$

Now that we have the two qubits initialised we can now apply a Hadamard gate to our control qubit. Now there's a problem. How do we apply a Hadamard gate to our control qubit when it is part of a 2 qubit state? The best solution is to expand out the Hadamard gates matrix so that we can apply it to our two qubit state. This can be done by finding the Kronecker product of the Hadamard gate and Identity gate.

Remember the Hadamard gate matrix is:

$$H = \frac{1}{\sqrt{2}} \begin{bmatrix} 1 & 1 \\ 1 & -1 \end{bmatrix} \tag{6.7}$$

and the Identity gate matrix:

$$I = \begin{bmatrix} 1 & 0 \\ 0 & 1 \end{bmatrix} \tag{6.8}$$

Then the Kronecker product is: $H \otimes I = \frac{1}{\sqrt{2}} \begin{bmatrix} 1 & 1 \\ 1 & -1 \end{bmatrix} \otimes \begin{bmatrix} 1 & 0 \\ 0 & 1 \end{bmatrix}$

$$= \frac{1}{\sqrt{2}} \begin{bmatrix} 1(1) & 1(0) & 1(1) & 1(0) \\ 1(0) & 1(1) & 1(0) & 1(1) \\ 1(1) & 1(0) & -1(1) & -1(0) \\ 1(0) & 1(1) & -1(0) & -1(1) \end{bmatrix} = \frac{1}{\sqrt{2}} \begin{bmatrix} 1 & 0 & 1 & 0 \\ 0 & 1 & 0 & 1 \\ 1 & 0 & -1 & 0 \\ 0 & 1 & 0 & -1 \end{bmatrix}$$

(6.9)

Next we need to multiply the above matrix by our initialised qubit state:

$$\frac{1}{\sqrt{2}} \begin{bmatrix} 1 & 0 & 1 & 0 \\ 0 & 1 & 0 & 1 \\ 1 & 0 & -1 & 0 \\ 0 & 1 & 0 & -1 \end{bmatrix} \begin{bmatrix} 1 \\ 0 \\ 0 \\ 0 \end{bmatrix}$$

(6.10)

$$= \frac{1}{\sqrt{2}} \begin{bmatrix} 1(1) + 0(0) + 1(0) + 0(0) \\ 0(1) + 1(0) + 0(0) + 0(0) \\ 1(1) + 0(0) + -1(0) + 0(0) \\ 0(1) + 1(0) + 0(0) + -1(0) \end{bmatrix} = \frac{1}{\sqrt{2}} \begin{bmatrix} 1 \\ 0 \\ 1 \\ 0 \end{bmatrix}$$

(6.11)

Now we just need to apply the CNOT gate to the circuit by multiplying the state above with the CNOT matrix:

$$\begin{bmatrix} 1 & 0 & 0 & 0 \\ 0 & 1 & 0 & 0 \\ 0 & 0 & 0 & 1 \\ 0 & 0 & 1 & 0 \end{bmatrix} \frac{1}{\sqrt{2}} \begin{bmatrix} 1 \\ 0 \\ 1 \\ 0 \end{bmatrix} = \frac{1}{\sqrt{2}} \begin{bmatrix} 1(1) + 0(0) + 0(1) + 0(0) \\ 0(1) + 1(0) + 0(1) + 0(0) \\ 0(1) + 0(0) + 0(1) + 1(0) \\ 0(1) + 0(0) + 1(1) + 0(0) \end{bmatrix} = \frac{1}{\sqrt{2}} \begin{bmatrix} 1 \\ 0 \\ 0 \\ 1 \end{bmatrix}$$

(6.12)

Which finally gives us the state:

$$\frac{|00\rangle + |11\rangle}{\sqrt{2}}$$

(6.13)

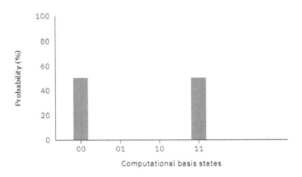

Figure 6.3: Probability distribution of bell states

6.3 Phase Kickback

From the previous section we can see that if we apply a Bell circuit we will get the state $\frac{|00\rangle + |11\rangle}{\sqrt{2}}$. However what if we apply a closing hadamard gate to the control qubit we get a very interesting result. From the last section we know that a bell circuit will give us the following statvector:

$$\frac{1}{\sqrt{2}} \begin{bmatrix} 1 \\ 0 \\ 0 \\ 1 \end{bmatrix} \tag{6.14}$$

If we apply a closing hadamard gate:

$$\frac{1}{\sqrt{2}} \begin{bmatrix} 1 \\ 0 \\ 0 \\ 1 \end{bmatrix} \frac{1}{\sqrt{2}} \begin{bmatrix} 1 & 0 & 1 & 0 \\ 0 & 1 & 0 & 1 \\ 1 & 0 & -1 & 0 \\ 0 & 1 & 0 & -1 \end{bmatrix} \tag{6.15}$$

$$= \frac{1}{2} \begin{bmatrix} 1(1) + 0(0) + 0(1) + 0(1) \\ 1(0) + 0(1) + 0(0) + 1(1) \\ 1(1) + 0(0) + 0(-1) + 1(0) \\ 1(0) + 0(1) + 0(0) + 1(-1) \end{bmatrix} = \frac{1}{2} \begin{bmatrix} 1 \\ 1 \\ 1 \\ -1 \end{bmatrix} \qquad (6.16)$$

Which gives us the state $\frac{1}{2}(|00\rangle + |01\rangle + |10\rangle - |11\rangle)$ But hold on! Why do we have a negative phase for $|11\rangle$? This is known as phase kickback and it is a very interesting phenomena that has profound implications when dealing with entangled states.

Let's see phase kickback in action with the following circuit:

Let's first initialise our 2 qubit system to $|00\rangle$:

$$|00\rangle = \begin{bmatrix} 1 \\ 0 \\ 0 \\ 0 \end{bmatrix} \qquad (6.17)$$

Next we need to apply the Pauli X gate to the second qubit. This will gives us the state vector:

$$|01\rangle = \begin{bmatrix} 0 \\ 1 \\ 0 \\ 0 \end{bmatrix} \qquad (6.18)$$

Next we need to apply the two hadamard gates. This can be done by getting the kronecker product of the hadamard gate matrix by itself:

$$H \otimes H = \frac{1}{\sqrt{2}} \begin{bmatrix} 1 & 1 \\ 1 & -1 \end{bmatrix} \otimes \frac{1}{\sqrt{2}} \begin{bmatrix} 1 & 1 \\ 1 & -1 \end{bmatrix} \qquad (6.19)$$

Which gives us the matrix:

$$\frac{1}{2} \begin{bmatrix} 1 & 1 & 1 & 1 \\ 1 & -1 & 1 & -1 \\ 1 & 1 & -1 & -1 \\ 1 & -1 & -1 & 1 \end{bmatrix} \qquad (6.20)$$

Now we just need to multiply our statevector with the matrix above to apply the parallel hadamard gates:

$$\frac{1}{2} \begin{bmatrix} 1 & 1 & 1 & 1 \\ 1 & -1 & 1 & -1 \\ 1 & 1 & -1 & -1 \\ 1 & -1 & -1 & 1 \end{bmatrix} \begin{bmatrix} 0 \\ 1 \\ 0 \\ 0 \end{bmatrix} \qquad (6.21)$$

$$= \frac{1}{2} \begin{bmatrix} 1(0) + 1(1) + 1(0) + 1(0) \\ 1(0) + -1(1) + 1(0) + -1(0) \\ 1(0) + 1(1) + -1(0) + -1(0) \\ 1(0) + -1(1) + -1(0) + 1(0) \end{bmatrix} = \frac{1}{2} \begin{bmatrix} 1 \\ -1 \\ 1 \\ -1 \end{bmatrix} \qquad (6.22)$$

Which gives us the statevector:

$$\frac{1}{2}\begin{bmatrix} 1 \\ -1 \\ 1 \\ -1 \end{bmatrix} \tag{6.23}$$

Where $|01\rangle$ and $|11\rangle$ have a negative phase! Now we just need to apply the CNOT gate:

$$\begin{bmatrix} 1 & 0 & 0 & 0 \\ 0 & 1 & 0 & 0 \\ 0 & 0 & 0 & 1 \\ 0 & 0 & 1 & 0 \end{bmatrix} \frac{1}{2}\begin{bmatrix} 1 \\ -1 \\ 1 \\ -1 \end{bmatrix} \tag{6.24}$$

$$\frac{1}{2}\begin{bmatrix} 1(1)+0(-1)+0(1)+0(-1) \\ 0(1)+1(-1)+0(1)+0(-1) \\ 0(1)+0(-1)+0(1)+1(-1) \\ 0(1)+0(-1)+1(1)+0(-1) \end{bmatrix} = \frac{1}{2}\begin{bmatrix} 1 \\ -1 \\ -1 \\ 1 \end{bmatrix} \tag{6.25}$$

and now if we apply the closing hadamard gate for q_0 we will get back $|10\rangle$!

$$\frac{1}{2}\begin{bmatrix} 1 & 1 & 1 & 1 \\ 1 & -1 & 1 & -1 \\ 1 & 1 & -1 & -1 \\ 1 & -1 & -1 & 1 \end{bmatrix} \frac{1}{2}\begin{bmatrix} 1 \\ -1 \\ -1 \\ 1 \end{bmatrix} \tag{6.26}$$

$$= \frac{1}{4}\begin{bmatrix} 1(1)+1(-1)+1(-1)+1(1) \\ 1(1)+-1(-1)+1(-1)+-1(1) \\ 1(1)+1(-1)+-1(-1)+-1(1) \\ 1(1)+-1(-1)+-1(-1)+1(1) \end{bmatrix} = \frac{1}{4}\begin{bmatrix} 0 \\ 0 \\ 0 \\ 4 \end{bmatrix} = \begin{bmatrix} 0 \\ 0 \\ 0 \\ 1 \end{bmatrix} \tag{6.27}$$

From this we can see that because we gave the target qubit a negative phase by applying a Pauli X gate and then putting in to superposition our state will become $|11\rangle$! Phase kickback is a very powerful phenomenon that it used in many quantum algorithms most notably the Phase estimation algorithm.

6.4 GHZ Circuit

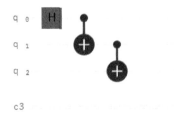

Figure 6.4: Circuit diagram of the GHZ circuit

The GHZ (Greenberger–Horne–Zeilinger) circuit is an extension of the Bell circuit developed by Daniel Greenberger, Michael Horne and Anton Zeilinger in their 1989 paper [10]. The GHZ circuit is functionally the same as the Bell circuit except that it includes a third qubit. Where the Bell state is $\frac{|00\rangle+|11\rangle}{\sqrt{2}}$ the GHZ circuit state is instead $\frac{|000\rangle+|111\rangle}{\sqrt{2}}$

Like with the Bell circuit lets see how our the circuit affects the state of the system by going through the matrix multiplication. The first step will be the same as with the Bell circuit where we had to get the Kronecker product: $H \otimes I$. However since the GHZ circuit is a 3 qubit system we have to expand H to become a 8X8 matrix.

We already know the 4X4 matrix for the Hadamard gate is:

$$\frac{1}{\sqrt{2}} \begin{bmatrix} 1 & 0 & 1 & 0 \\ 0 & 1 & 0 & 1 \\ 1 & 0 & -1 & 0 \\ 0 & 1 & 0 & -1 \end{bmatrix} \tag{6.28}$$

So how do we expand the hadamard matrix for our 3 qubit system? Simple, just get the kronecker product of the hadamard matrix above with the identity gate.

Remember the Identity gate is :

$$I = \begin{bmatrix} 1 & 0 \\ 0 & 1 \end{bmatrix} \tag{6.29}$$

So $H \otimes I$:

$$\frac{1}{\sqrt{2}} \begin{bmatrix} 1 & 0 & 1 & 0 \\ 0 & 1 & 0 & 1 \\ 1 & 0 & -1 & 0 \\ 0 & 1 & 0 & -1 \end{bmatrix} \otimes \begin{bmatrix} 1 & 0 \\ 0 & 1 \end{bmatrix} \tag{6.30}$$

$$= \frac{1}{\sqrt{2}} \begin{bmatrix} 1 & 0 & 0 & 0 & 1 & 0 & 0 & 0 \\ 0 & 1 & 0 & 0 & 0 & 1 & 0 & 0 \\ 0 & 0 & 1 & 0 & 0 & 0 & 1 & 0 \\ 0 & 0 & 0 & 1 & 0 & 0 & 0 & 1 \\ 1 & 0 & 0 & 0 & -1 & 0 & 0 & 0 \\ 0 & 1 & 0 & 0 & 0 & -1 & 0 & 0 \\ 0 & 0 & 1 & 0 & 0 & 0 & -1 & 0 \\ 0 & 0 & 0 & 1 & 0 & 0 & 0 & -1 \end{bmatrix} \qquad (6.31)$$

Finally we have our 8X8 hadamard gate for our GHZ circuit. Now let's initialise all our qubits to $|0\rangle$ and apply the hadamard gate to our first qubit. If all qubits are initialised to $|0\rangle$ then the associated column matrix will be:

$$|000\rangle = \begin{bmatrix} 1 \\ 0 \\ 0 \\ 0 \\ 0 \\ 0 \\ 0 \\ 0 \end{bmatrix}$$

Now we just need to apply our Hadamard gate to the first qubit:

$$\frac{1}{\sqrt{2}} \begin{bmatrix} 1 & 0 & 0 & 0 & 1 & 0 & 0 & 0 \\ 0 & 1 & 0 & 0 & 0 & 1 & 0 & 0 \\ 0 & 0 & 1 & 0 & 0 & 0 & 1 & 0 \\ 0 & 0 & 0 & 1 & 0 & 0 & 0 & 1 \\ 1 & 0 & 0 & 0 & -1 & 0 & 0 & 0 \\ 0 & 1 & 0 & 0 & 0 & -1 & 0 & 0 \\ 0 & 0 & 1 & 0 & 0 & 0 & -1 & 0 \\ 0 & 0 & 0 & 1 & 0 & 0 & 0 & -1 \end{bmatrix} \begin{bmatrix} 1 \\ 0 \\ 0 \\ 0 \\ 0 \\ 0 \\ 0 \\ 0 \end{bmatrix} = \frac{1}{\sqrt{2}} \begin{bmatrix} 1 \\ 0 \\ 0 \\ 0 \\ 1 \\ 0 \\ 0 \\ 0 \end{bmatrix} \qquad (6.32)$$

Next we a need to apply the first CNOT gate. However the CNOT gate matrix is only 4X4 and we need it to be 8X8 for the 3 qubit system. As such we need to get the kronecker product of the CNOT gate and the identity gate:

$$CNOT \otimes I = \begin{bmatrix} 1 & 0 & 0 & 0 \\ 0 & 1 & 0 & 0 \\ 0 & 0 & 0 & 1 \\ 0 & 0 & 1 & 0 \end{bmatrix} \otimes \begin{bmatrix} 1 & 0 \\ 0 & 1 \end{bmatrix} \tag{6.33}$$

The resulting product is :

$$CNOT = \begin{bmatrix} 1 & 0 & 0 & 0 & 0 & 0 & 0 & 0 \\ 0 & 1 & 0 & 0 & 0 & 0 & 0 & 0 \\ 0 & 0 & 1 & 0 & 0 & 0 & 0 & 0 \\ 0 & 0 & 0 & 1 & 0 & 0 & 0 & 0 \\ 0 & 0 & 0 & 0 & 0 & 0 & 1 & 0 \\ 0 & 0 & 0 & 0 & 0 & 0 & 0 & 1 \\ 0 & 0 & 0 & 0 & 1 & 0 & 0 & 0 \\ 0 & 0 & 0 & 0 & 0 & 1 & 0 & 0 \end{bmatrix} \tag{6.34}$$

Now let's apply the 8X8 CNOT gate above with our quantum state:

$$\begin{bmatrix} 1 & 0 & 0 & 0 & 0 & 0 & 0 & 0 \\ 0 & 1 & 0 & 0 & 0 & 0 & 0 & 0 \\ 0 & 0 & 1 & 0 & 0 & 0 & 0 & 0 \\ 0 & 0 & 0 & 1 & 0 & 0 & 0 & 0 \\ 0 & 0 & 0 & 0 & 0 & 0 & 1 & 0 \\ 0 & 0 & 0 & 0 & 0 & 0 & 0 & 1 \\ 0 & 0 & 0 & 0 & 1 & 0 & 0 & 0 \\ 0 & 0 & 0 & 0 & 0 & 1 & 0 & 0 \end{bmatrix} \frac{1}{\sqrt{2}} \begin{bmatrix} 1 \\ 0 \\ 0 \\ 0 \\ 1 \\ 0 \\ 0 \\ 0 \end{bmatrix} = \frac{1}{\sqrt{2}} \begin{bmatrix} 1 \\ 0 \\ 0 \\ 0 \\ 0 \\ 0 \\ 1 \\ 0 \end{bmatrix} \tag{6.35}$$

Which is equal to $\frac{|000\rangle+|110\rangle}{\sqrt{2}}$ but the GHZ circuits state should be $\frac{|000\rangle+|111\rangle}{\sqrt{2}}$! Well we just need to apply the second CNOT gate.

$$
\begin{bmatrix}
1 & 0 & 0 & 0 & 0 & 0 & 0 & 0 \\
0 & 1 & 0 & 0 & 0 & 0 & 0 & 0 \\
0 & 0 & 1 & 0 & 0 & 0 & 0 & 0 \\
0 & 0 & 0 & 1 & 0 & 0 & 0 & 0 \\
0 & 0 & 0 & 0 & 0 & 0 & 1 & 0 \\
0 & 0 & 0 & 0 & 0 & 0 & 0 & 1 \\
0 & 0 & 0 & 0 & 1 & 0 & 0 & 0 \\
0 & 0 & 0 & 0 & 0 & 1 & 0 & 0
\end{bmatrix}
\frac{1}{\sqrt{2}}
\begin{bmatrix}1\\0\\0\\0\\0\\0\\1\\0\end{bmatrix}
=
\frac{1}{\sqrt{2}}
\begin{bmatrix}1\\0\\0\\0\\0\\0\\0\\1\end{bmatrix}
\tag{6.36}
$$

Which finally maps to $\frac{|000\rangle+|111\rangle}{\sqrt{2}}$!

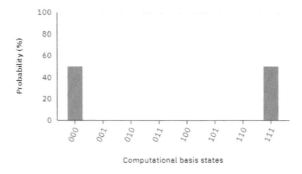

Figure 6.5: Probability distribution of GHZ circuit

6.5 W State Circuit

Figure 6.6: Circuit diagram of the W state circuit

Another interesting three qubit circuit is the W state circuit. It is named after one of the discoverers Wolfgang Dür along with Guifré Vidal, and Ignacio Cirac. This circuit is very similar to the GHZ circuit in that it entangles 3 qubits together. However instead of the states mapping to $\frac{|000\rangle + |111\rangle}{\sqrt{2}}$ it instead maps to:

$$|W\rangle = \frac{1}{\sqrt{3}}(|001\rangle + |010\rangle + |100\rangle) \qquad (6.37)$$

This means that are three possible states where each state has 1 qubit set to $|1\rangle$ while the rest are set to $|0\rangle$.

7 Quantum Algorithms

Quantum algorithms may be "pure" quantum algorithms that can be fully described using quantum circuits alone. However many quantum algorithms are hybrid algorithms that may use a classical computers for specific calculations.

7.1 The Deutsch-Jozsa algorithm

The Deutsch-Jozsa algorithm developed by David Deutsch and Richard Jozsa[8] is a quantum algorithm that determines if a function is either balanced or constant. This algorithm was one of the first quantum algorithms that was proven to have a clear advantage over it's classical counterpart. That is because the algorithm only requires one query while a classical solution requires in a worst case scenario $2^{n-1} + 1$ queries.

Consider a function $f : \{0,1\}^n \rightarrow \{0,1\}$ where the input is a bit string of N size. The function can be either balanced or constant. Balanced means that exactly half of the possible bit strings will return 0 and the other half will return 1. If it is constant then all inputs will return 0 or all will return 1. For example consider a 3 bit string.

If the function is constant then its truth table will look like so:

A	B	C	f(x)
0	0	0	1
0	0	1	1
0	1	0	1
0	1	1	1
1	0	0	1
1	0	1	1
1	1	0	1
1	1	1	1

Table 7.1: Truth table for a constant function that returns 1 for all inputs

If the function is balanced then the truth table may look like so:

A	B	C	f(x)
0	0	0	0
0	0	1	1
0	1	0	0
0	1	1	1
1	0	0	0
1	0	1	1
1	1	0	0
1	1	1	1

Table 7.2: Truth table for a balanced function that returns 1 for half of the inputs and 0 for the other half

7.1.1 How the algorithm works

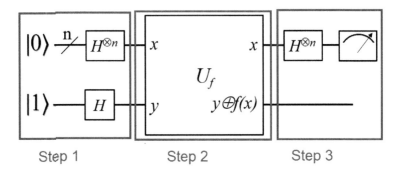

Step 1   Step 2   Step 3

Figure 7.1: Circuit diagram of Deutsch-Jozsa circuit

The algorithm itself is fairly simple and uses the circuit in the figure above. It consists of two registers. The first register is the one that holds the bit string. All qubits in this register are set to $|0\rangle$. The second register consists of only 1 qubit that is set to $|1\rangle$. An oracle is then applied that maps $x \rightarrow x$ and $y \rightarrow y \oplus f(x)$. Where x conists of the qubits associated with register 1 and y is the qubit associated with register 2.

Step 1: Initialise the qubits

The first step is to put all the qubits in to their initial state. For this the bit string qubits in the first register are set to $|0\rangle$ and the qubit in the second register is set to $|1\rangle$. Next all qubits are put in to superposition by applying a hadamard gate to each.

Step 2: Apply the Oracle

The next step is to apply something called an oracle. An oracle is just a part of the circuit used to map a set of inputs to a set of outputs. In the case of this algorithm it maps $x \to x$ and $y \to y \oplus f(x)$. There are two oracles we can implement. An oracle to find out if the function is balanced and another oracle to find out if the function is constant.

If we want to find out if the function is balanced we can setup an oracle that consists of CNOTs:

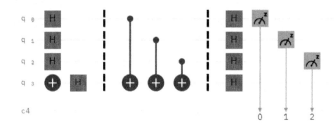

Figure 7.2: Oracle for a balanced function

If we want to check if the function is constant then we apply an X gate to y if f(x) is 1 else we use an Identity gate on y if f(x) is 0:

Step 3: Apply closing hadamard gates

The final step is to apply closing hadamard gates to all qubits and then measure register 1.

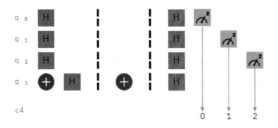

Figure 7.3: Circuit for a constant function if f(x) = 1

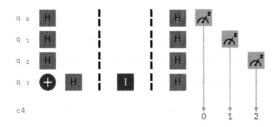

Figure 7.4: Circuit for a constant function if f(x) = 0

7.2 Bernstein-Vazirani Algorithm

The Barnstein Vazirani algorithm that is very similar in style to the Deutsch-Jozsra algorithm. However instead of finding out if a function is balanced or constant it instead evaluates a hidden string. Like the Deutsch-Jozsra algorithm it takes the following function $f : \{0,1\}^n \rightarrow \{0,1\}$ that takes a bitstring of N size and will return either 0 or 1.

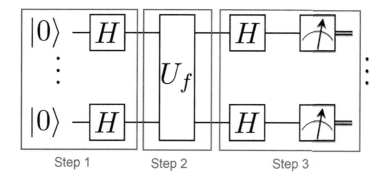

Step 1   Step 2   Step 3

Figure 7.5: Circuit diagram for Bernstein-Vazirani algorithm

7.2.1 How the algorithm works

Since the Bernstein-Vazirani is an extension of the Deutsch-Jozsra algorithm it has similar steps and a similar circuit. The circuit consists of two registers. Register 1 holds the bit string and consists of N qubits for N bits in bitstring. Register 2 consists of only 1 qubit.

Step 1: Put the qubits in to superposition by applying hadamard gates

The first step is to initialise the qubits and put them in to superposition. The qubits have to be initialised to $|0\rangle$. Then all qubits are put in to superposition using hadamard gates. Then the qubit in register 2 is set $|-\rangle$ using a Z gate.

Step 2: Apply the oracle

The next step is to apply the oracle in order to find the hidden string. To do this CNOT are applied where the target qubit is the qubit in register 2. The control qubits are the qubits that correspond to the bits in the bit string that equal 1. If the bit is 0 then an identity gate is applied to the corresponding qubit.

Step 3: Apply closing Hadamard gates

The last step is apply the closing hadamard gates to register 1 and measure the qubits. The full circuit is in the figure below.

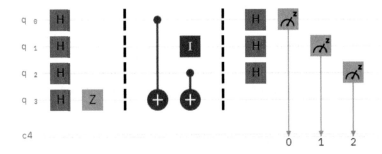

Figure 7.6: Oracle to find 101

7.3 Superdense Coding

Superdense coding is a quantum communication protocol proposed by Bennett and Wiesner in a paper in 1992 [3] for sending two classical bits down a communication channel using only 1 qubit.

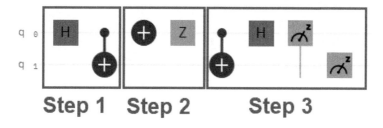

Figure 7.7: Circuit diagram of the Superdense Coding protocol.

7.3.1 Protocol

The protocol can be broken down in to the following steps.

Step 1: Prepare a Bell pair

In this step a bell pair consisting of two qubits is prepared. A bell pair is simply an entangled pair of qubits which are entangled by applying a Hadamard gate and to q_0 and then applying a CNOT gate to q_1 where the control qubit is q_0.

q_0

q_1

Figure 7.8: Circuit diagram of a Bell pair.

From the previous section on Bell circuits we know that this will transform the state such that:

$$\begin{bmatrix} 1 \\ 0 \\ 0 \\ 0 \end{bmatrix} \rightarrow \frac{1}{\sqrt{2}} \begin{bmatrix} 1 \\ 0 \\ 0 \\ 1 \end{bmatrix} \tag{7.1}$$

Step 2: Encoding the classical bits

After the qubits have been sent the classical bits are encoded on to q_0 using quantum logic gates. For this different quantum logic gates are applied based on what states the user wants to encode.

If the user wants to apply 00 then they apply an identity gate.

$$\frac{1}{\sqrt{2}} \begin{bmatrix} 1 \\ 0 \\ 0 \\ 1 \end{bmatrix} \begin{bmatrix} 1 & 0 & 0 & 0 \\ 0 & 1 & 0 & 0 \\ 0 & 0 & 1 & 0 \\ 0 & 0 & 0 & 1 \end{bmatrix} = \frac{1}{\sqrt{2}} \begin{bmatrix} 1 \\ 0 \\ 0 \\ 1 \end{bmatrix} \tag{7.2}$$

If the user wants to apply 01 then they apply an Pauli-X gate.

$$\frac{1}{\sqrt{2}}\begin{bmatrix}1\\0\\0\\1\end{bmatrix}\begin{bmatrix}0&0&1&0\\0&0&0&1\\1&0&0&0\\0&1&0&0\end{bmatrix}=\frac{1}{\sqrt{2}}\begin{bmatrix}0\\1\\1\\0\end{bmatrix}$$

(7.3)

If the user wants to apply 10 then they apply a Pauli-Z gate.

$$\frac{1}{\sqrt{2}}\begin{bmatrix}1\\0\\0\\1\end{bmatrix}\begin{bmatrix}1&0&0&0\\0&1&0&0\\0&0&-1&0\\0&0&0&-1\end{bmatrix}=\frac{1}{\sqrt{2}}\begin{bmatrix}1\\0\\0\\-1\end{bmatrix}$$

(7.4)

If the user wants to apply 11 then they apply a Pauli-Z gate followed by a Pauli-X gate

Applying the Z-gate:

$$\frac{1}{\sqrt{2}}\begin{bmatrix}1\\0\\0\\1\end{bmatrix}\begin{bmatrix}1&0&0&0\\0&1&0&0\\0&0&-1&0\\0&0&0&-1\end{bmatrix}=\frac{1}{\sqrt{2}}\begin{bmatrix}1\\0\\0\\-1\end{bmatrix}$$

(7.5)

Then the X-gate:

$$\frac{1}{\sqrt{2}}\begin{bmatrix}1\\0\\0\\-1\end{bmatrix}\begin{bmatrix}0&0&1&0\\0&0&0&1\\1&0&0&0\\0&1&0&0\end{bmatrix}=\frac{1}{\sqrt{2}}\begin{bmatrix}0\\-1\\1\\0\end{bmatrix}$$

(7.6)

Step 3: Decoding

Next the classical bits have to be decoded. To do this a CNOT gate is applied to q_1 where q_0 is the control qubit. Next a Hadamard gate is applied to q_0 to bring it out of superposition.

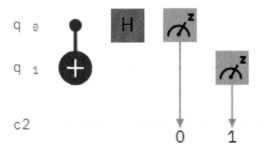

Figure 7.9: Step 3 of the protocol

For example if we encoded 00 then we apply a CNOT gate and hadamard gate like so:

$$\begin{bmatrix} 1 & 0 & 0 & 0 \\ 0 & 1 & 0 & 0 \\ 0 & 0 & 0 & 1 \\ 0 & 0 & 1 & 0 \end{bmatrix} \frac{1}{\sqrt{2}} \begin{bmatrix} 1 \\ 0 \\ 0 \\ 1 \end{bmatrix} = \frac{1}{\sqrt{2}} \begin{bmatrix} 1(1) + 0(0) + 0(0) + 0(1) \\ 0(1) + 1(0) + 0(0) + 0(1) \\ 0(1) + 0(0) + 0(0) + 1(1) \\ 0(1) + 0(0) + 1(0) + 0(1) \end{bmatrix} = \frac{1}{\sqrt{2}} \begin{bmatrix} 1 \\ 0 \\ 1 \\ 0 \end{bmatrix}$$

(7.7)

Then apply the closing hadamard gate:

$$\frac{1}{\sqrt{2}} \begin{bmatrix} 1 & 0 & 1 & 0 \\ 0 & 1 & 0 & 1 \\ 1 & 0 & -1 & 0 \\ 0 & 1 & 0 & -1 \end{bmatrix} \frac{1}{\sqrt{2}} \begin{bmatrix} 1 \\ 0 \\ 1 \\ 0 \end{bmatrix} \tag{7.8}$$

$$= \frac{1}{\sqrt{2}} \frac{1}{\sqrt{2}} \begin{bmatrix} 1(1) + 0(0) + 1(1) + 0(0) \\ 0(1) + 1(0) + 0(1) + 1(0) \\ 1(1) + 0(0) + -1(1) + 0(0) \\ 0(1) + 1(0) + 0(1) + -1(0) \end{bmatrix} = \begin{bmatrix} 1 \\ 0 \\ 0 \\ 0 \end{bmatrix} \tag{7.9}$$

Where the measured state is $|00\rangle$

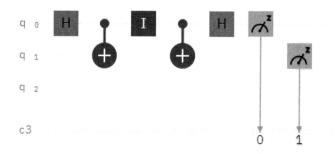

Figure 7.10: Entire circuit for encoding $|00\rangle$

If we encoded 01 on to the qubit then again we apply a CNOT and hadamard gate like so:

$$\begin{bmatrix} 1 & 0 & 0 & 0 \\ 0 & 1 & 0 & 0 \\ 0 & 0 & 0 & 1 \\ 0 & 0 & 1 & 0 \end{bmatrix} \frac{1}{\sqrt{2}} \begin{bmatrix} 0 \\ 1 \\ 1 \\ 0 \end{bmatrix} = \frac{1}{\sqrt{2}} \begin{bmatrix} 1(0) + 0(1) + 0(1) + 0(0) \\ 0(0) + 1(1) + 0(1) + 0(0) \\ 0(0) + 0(1) + 0(1) + 1(0) \\ 0(0) + 0(1) + 1(1) + 0(0) \end{bmatrix} = \frac{1}{\sqrt{2}} \begin{bmatrix} 0 \\ 1 \\ 0 \\ 1 \end{bmatrix}$$

$$(7.10)$$

and then if we encode the closing hadamard gate:

$$\frac{1}{\sqrt{2}} \begin{bmatrix} 1 & 0 & 1 & 0 \\ 0 & 1 & 0 & 1 \\ 1 & 0 & -1 & 0 \\ 0 & 1 & 0 & -1 \end{bmatrix} \frac{1}{\sqrt{2}} \begin{bmatrix} 0 \\ 1 \\ 0 \\ 1 \end{bmatrix}$$

$$(7.11)$$

$$= \frac{1}{\sqrt{2}} \frac{1}{\sqrt{2}} \begin{bmatrix} 1(0) + 0(1) + 1(0) + 0(1) \\ 0(0) + 1(1) + 0(0) + 1(1) \\ 1(0) + 0(1) + -1(0) + 0(1) \\ 0(0) + 1(1) + 0(0) + -1(1) \end{bmatrix} = \begin{bmatrix} 0 \\ 1 \\ 0 \\ 0 \end{bmatrix}$$

$$(7.12)$$

Which gives us back the $|01\rangle$ that we encoded!

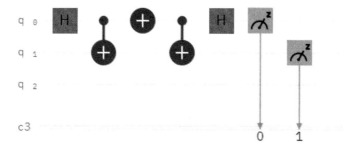

Figure 7.11: Entire circuit for encoding $|01\rangle$

If we encoded $|10\rangle$ then we again apply a CNOT gate and closing hadamard gate:

$$\begin{bmatrix} 1 & 0 & 0 & 0 \\ 0 & 1 & 0 & 0 \\ 0 & 0 & 0 & 1 \\ 0 & 0 & 1 & 0 \end{bmatrix} \frac{1}{\sqrt{2}} \begin{bmatrix} 1 \\ 0 \\ 0 \\ -1 \end{bmatrix} = \frac{1}{\sqrt{2}} \begin{bmatrix} 1(1)+0(0)+0(0)+0(-1) \\ 0(1)+1(0)+0(0)+0(-1) \\ 0(1)+0(0)+0(0)+1(-1) \\ 0(1)+0(0)+1(0)+0(-1) \end{bmatrix} = \frac{1}{\sqrt{2}} \begin{bmatrix} 1 \\ 0 \\ -1 \\ 0 \end{bmatrix}$$
(7.13)

Now if we apply the closing hadamard gate:

$$\frac{1}{\sqrt{2}} \begin{bmatrix} 1 & 0 & 1 & 0 \\ 0 & 1 & 0 & 1 \\ 1 & 0 & -1 & 0 \\ 0 & 1 & 0 & -1 \end{bmatrix} \frac{1}{\sqrt{2}} \begin{bmatrix} 1 \\ 0 \\ -1 \\ 0 \end{bmatrix}$$
(7.14)

$$= \frac{1}{\sqrt{2}} \frac{1}{\sqrt{2}} \begin{bmatrix} 1(1)+0(0)+1(-1)+0(0) \\ 0(1)+1(0)+0(-1)+1(0) \\ 1(1)+0(0)+-1(-1)+0(0) \\ 0(1)+1(0)+0(-1)+-1(0) \end{bmatrix} = \begin{bmatrix} 0 \\ 0 \\ 1 \\ 0 \end{bmatrix}$$
(7.15)

Which gives us back the $|10\rangle$ state that we encoded!

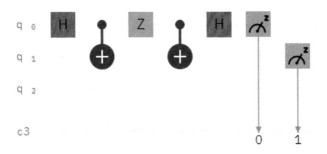

Figure 7.12: Entire circuit for encoding $|10\rangle$

And finally if we encoded $|11\rangle$ then we do the same;

$$
\begin{bmatrix} 1 & 0 & 0 & 0 \\ 0 & 1 & 0 & 0 \\ 0 & 0 & 0 & 1 \\ 0 & 0 & 1 & 0 \end{bmatrix} \frac{1}{\sqrt{2}} \begin{bmatrix} 0 \\ -1 \\ 1 \\ 0 \end{bmatrix} \tag{7.16}
$$

$$
= \frac{1}{\sqrt{2}} \begin{bmatrix} 1(0) + 0(-1) + 0(1) + 0(0) \\ 0(0) + 1(-1) + 0(1) + 0(0) \\ 0(0) + 0(-1) + 0(1) + 1(0) \\ 0(0) + 0(-1) + 1(1) + 0(0) \end{bmatrix} = \frac{1}{\sqrt{2}} \begin{bmatrix} 0 \\ -1 \\ 0 \\ 1 \end{bmatrix} \tag{7.17}
$$

then if we apply the closing hadamard gate:

$$\frac{1}{\sqrt{2}}\begin{bmatrix} 1 & 0 & 1 & 0 \\ 0 & 1 & 0 & 1 \\ 1 & 0 & -1 & 0 \\ 0 & 1 & 0 & -1 \end{bmatrix} \frac{1}{\sqrt{2}}\begin{bmatrix} 0 \\ -1 \\ 0 \\ 1 \end{bmatrix} \qquad (7.18)$$

$$= \frac{1}{\sqrt{2}}\frac{1}{\sqrt{2}}\begin{bmatrix} 1(0) + 0(-1) + 1(0) + 0(1) \\ 0(0) + 1(-1) + 0(0) + 1(1) \\ 1(0) + 0(-1) + -1(0) + 0(1) \\ 0(0) + 1(-1) + 0(0) + -1(1) \end{bmatrix} = \begin{bmatrix} 0 \\ 0 \\ 0 \\ 1 \end{bmatrix} \qquad (7.19)$$

which has given back the $|11\rangle$ state that we encoded!

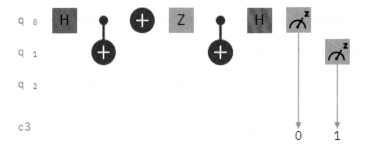

Figure 7.13: Entire circuit for encoding $|11\rangle$

7.4 Quantum Teleportation

Quantum teleportation is a communication method whereby a qubits state is transferred between two parties (known as Alice and Bob respectively) using classical bits. While Superdense coding transfers two classical bits using only one qubit quantum teleportation is the opposite in that it instead uses 2 classical bits to teleport a qubit as long as the two parties also share an entangled pair of qubits.

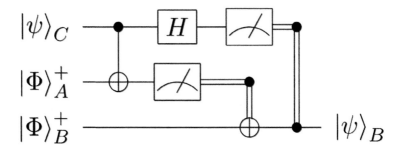

Figure 7.14: Quantum Teleportation Circuit.

7.4.1 Protocol

The protocol starts with three qubits. The first two are kept by Alice and are denoted as $|\psi\rangle_C$ and $|\phi\rangle_A$ respectively. $|\psi\rangle_C$ contains the state Alice wants to teleport to Bob and $|\phi\rangle_A$ is one half of the entangled pair. Bob only has the third qubit denoted as $|\phi\rangle_B$

Step 1: Generate a Bell pair

Like with the superdense coding protocol the first step is to create a bell pair consisting of two qubits. The first qubit is kept at location A while the second is sent to location B.

Step 2: Alice performs a Bell measurement

The second step is for Alice to perform a measurement of her two qubits $|\psi\rangle_C$ and $|\phi\rangle_A$. From this she will get four possible results $|00\rangle$, $|01\rangle$, $|10\rangle$, or $|11\rangle$. After she has obtained her measurements she sends the results in the form of two classical bits to Bob and then discards her qubits.

Step 3: Bob reconstructs the teleported state

After Bob has received the classical bits from Alice he can apply 4 different possible quantum logic gates on his qubit based on upon the results.

1. $00 \rightarrow I$

2. $01 \rightarrow X$

3. $10 \rightarrow Z$

4. $11 \rightarrow Y$

After applying these transformations Bob qubit should have the same state as $|\psi\rangle_C$ that Alice wanted to teleport!

7.5 Quantum Key Distribution using the BB84 protocol

Now that we have discussed both Superdense coding and Quantum Teleportation we can move on to Quantum Key Distribution (QKD). QKD is any method by which secret keys are generated and transmitted between two parties using qubits. The most famous of which is the BB84 protocol developed by Charles Bennett and Gilles Brassard in 1984. [2]

7.5.1 The Protocol

In the protocol there are two parties Alice and Bob. Alice the one who wants to generate and send the secret key while Bob is the one who will want to receive it.

Step 1: Alice generates a random bit string

The first step is for Alice to generate a string of bits for example 001110. Then she generates a string of N length consisting of basis states . These are either in the computational basis ie $|0\rangle, |1\rangle$ or the hadamard basis: $|+\rangle, |-\rangle$. For sake of brevity I will denote the computational basis as C and the hadamard basis as H. For example our bit string will be: 0011100 and the string holding our basis states will be CCCHCHC.

Step 2: Alice encodes her random bits

The second step is for Alice to encode each bit in her bit string to the corresponding basis in the basis string. For example if the first bit in her string is 0 and the corresponding basis is the computational basis then she leaves it as 0. If the bit is 0 and the basis is the hadamard basis she instead encodes the 0 as $|+\rangle$. See the table below for how the bits are encoded.

Bit String	0	0	1	1	1	0	1
Basis	C	C	H	C	H	H	C
Encoded bits	$|0\rangle$	$|0\rangle$	$|-\rangle$	$|1\rangle$	$|-\rangle$	$|+\rangle$	$|1\rangle$

Table 7.3:

The example above can be enocoded using the quantum circuit in the figure below.

Step 3: Bob measures each qubit

After Alice has finished encoding her bits she will send the qubits off down a secure authenticated channel down to Bob. Once Bob receives them he will just need to measure each qubit. However there is a caveat in that bob does not know the correct basis for each qubit in order to measure them. As such he has to guess. If the qubit is in the computational basis then he will simply have to measure them. However if the qubit has been encoded in the hadamard basis he will first have to bring the qubit out of superposition with a hadamard gate and then measure it. If he does not get the basis correct then he will simply measure $|0\rangle$ or $|1\rangle$ with equal probability and get just get random bits.

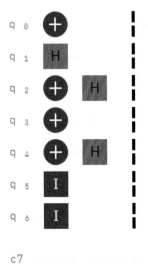

Figure 7.15: Entire circuit for encoding the example above

Step 4: Both parties share what basis they used

The next step is for both Alice and Bob to share which basis they used for which qubit. If both parties used the same basis for a qubit then they keep it in their key. However if the basis are different for that qubit then they discard it from their keys.

Step 5: Both parties compare and verify their keys

Next Alice and Bob share random samples of their keys. If the keys matched then the protocol has worked. However if

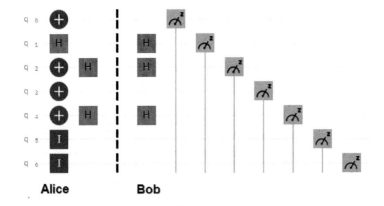

Figure 7.16: Entire circuit for encoding and measuring. Note here that Bob has correctly guessed each basis and so will fully reconstruct the bit string Alice has encoded

they do not match then it means the protocol has failed or the communication channel has been intercepted by a third party.

7.6 Quantum Fourier Transform

The Quantum Fourier Transform (QFT) is a linear transform that takes the state from the computational basis and maps it to the Fourier basis. In essence it encodes the state on to the phase of the qubit.

For example lets say we wanted to encode $|10\rangle$ in to the Fourier basis we could implement a QFT consisting of 2 qubits (q_1 and q_0). First a Pauli-X gate is applied to q_0 to create the state $|01\rangle$ such that the column vector will look like the following:

$$|10\rangle = \begin{bmatrix} 0 \\ 0 \\ 1 \\ 0 \end{bmatrix} \tag{7.20}$$

Next q_0 is put in to superposition using a hadamard gate such that the overall state will become:

$$\frac{|10\rangle + |11\rangle}{\sqrt{2}} = \frac{1}{\sqrt{2}} \begin{bmatrix} 0 \\ 0 \\ 1 \\ 1 \end{bmatrix} \tag{7.21}$$

Then a controlled U1 gate is applied where q_1 is the target and q_0 is the control. This will apply a rotation of $\pi/2$ to the target qubit. Where the matrix for the controlled U1 gate is:

$$CU1 = \begin{bmatrix} 1 & 0 & 0 & 0 \\ 0 & 1 & 0 & 0 \\ 0 & 0 & 1 & 0 \\ 0 & 0 & 0 & e^{i\left(\frac{\pi}{2}\right)} \end{bmatrix} \tag{7.22}$$

Applying this to the column vector gives us:

$$
\begin{bmatrix} 1 & 0 & 0 & 0 \\ 0 & 1 & 0 & 0 \\ 0 & 0 & 1 & 0 \\ 0 & 0 & 0 & e^{i(\frac{\pi}{2})} \end{bmatrix} \frac{1}{\sqrt{2}} \begin{bmatrix} 0 \\ 0 \\ 1 \\ 1 \end{bmatrix}
\tag{7.23}
$$

$$
= \frac{1}{\sqrt{2}} \begin{bmatrix} 1(0) + 0(0) + 0(1) + 0(1) \\ 0(0) + 1(0) + 0(1) + 0(1) \\ 0(0) + 0(0) + 1(1) + 0(1) \\ 0(0) + 0(0) + 0(1) + e^{i(\frac{\pi}{2})}(1) \end{bmatrix} = \frac{1}{\sqrt{2}} \begin{bmatrix} 0 \\ 0 \\ 1 \\ i \end{bmatrix}
\tag{7.24}
$$

Then a hadamard gate is applied to q_1:

$$
\frac{1}{\sqrt{2}} \begin{bmatrix} 1 & 0 & 1 & 0 \\ 0 & 1 & 0 & 1 \\ 1 & 0 & -1 & 0 \\ 0 & 1 & 0 & -1 \end{bmatrix} \frac{1}{\sqrt{2}} \begin{bmatrix} 0 \\ 0 \\ 1 \\ i \end{bmatrix}
\tag{7.25}
$$

$$
= \frac{1}{\sqrt{4}} \begin{bmatrix} 1(0) + 0(0) + 1(1) + 0(i) \\ 0(0) + 1(0) + 0(1) + 1(i) \\ 1(0) + 0(0) + -1(1) + 0(i) \\ 0(0) + 1(0) + 0(1) + -1(i) \end{bmatrix} = \frac{1}{\sqrt{4}} \begin{bmatrix} 1 \\ i \\ -1 \\ -i \end{bmatrix}
\tag{7.26}
$$

Which maps to the superposition state:

$$
\frac{|00\rangle + i|01\rangle - |10\rangle - i|11\rangle}{\sqrt{4}}
\tag{7.27}
$$

But why $\sqrt{4}$ and not $\sqrt{2}$? Well this is because there are 4 non-zero states that are possible and since the total probability must add up to 1 the probability of each possible state should be 0.25.

Next both qubits states are swapped using a SWAP gate. Remember that the Swap gate is represented by the following matrix:

$$SWAP = \begin{bmatrix} 1 & 0 & 0 & 0 \\ 0 & 0 & 1 & 0 \\ 0 & 1 & 0 & 0 \\ 0 & 0 & 0 & 1 \end{bmatrix} \tag{7.28}$$

Now to apply the SWAP gate:

$$\begin{bmatrix} 1 & 0 & 0 & 0 \\ 0 & 0 & 1 & 0 \\ 0 & 1 & 0 & 0 \\ 0 & 0 & 0 & 1 \end{bmatrix} \frac{1}{\sqrt{4}} \begin{bmatrix} 1 \\ i \\ -1 \\ -i \end{bmatrix} \tag{7.29}$$

$$= \frac{1}{\sqrt{4}} \begin{bmatrix} 1(1) + 0(i) + 0(-1) + 0(-i)) \\ 0(1) + 0(i) + 1(-1) + 0(-i) \\ 0(1) + 1(i) + 0(-1) + 0(-i) \\ 0(1) + 0(i) + 0(-1) + 1(-i) \end{bmatrix} = \frac{1}{\sqrt{4}} \begin{bmatrix} 1 \\ -1 \\ i \\ -i \end{bmatrix} \tag{7.30}$$

After this the state $|10\rangle$ is fully encoded in to the Fourier basis as:

$$\frac{|00\rangle - |01\rangle + i|10\rangle - i|11\rangle}{\sqrt{4}} \tag{7.31}$$

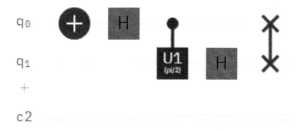

Figure 7.17: Circuit diagram of 2 qubit QFT.

If we measure the qubits now we will get random values
as the qubits are in superposition but the state we encoded is
within the phase. As such to put the state back in to the computational basis we need to use a circuit called the inverse QFT.
This is basically the reverse of the circuit we have already implemented. If we combine the QFT and decode it with an inverse
QFT we will get the state $|10\rangle$ when we measure the qubits.

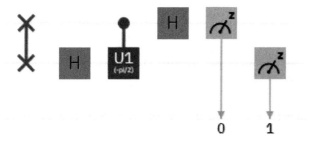

Figure 7.18: Circuit diagram of an inverse 2 qubit QFT.

Applying a swap gate to our last state:

$$
\begin{bmatrix} 1 & 0 & 0 & 0 \\ 0 & 0 & 1 & 0 \\ 0 & 1 & 0 & 0 \\ 0 & 0 & 0 & 1 \end{bmatrix} \frac{1}{\sqrt{4}} \begin{bmatrix} 1 \\ -1 \\ i \\ -i \end{bmatrix} \tag{7.32}
$$

$$
= \frac{1}{\sqrt{4}} \begin{bmatrix} 1(1) + 0(-1) + 0(i) + 0(-i)) \\ 0(1) + 0(-1) + 1(i) + 0(-i) \\ 0(1) + 1(-1) + 0(i) + 0(-i) \\ 0(1) + 0(-1) + 0(i) + 1(-i) \end{bmatrix} = \frac{1}{\sqrt{4}} \begin{bmatrix} 1 \\ i \\ -1 \\ -i \end{bmatrix} \tag{7.33}
$$

Which gives us back the state:

$$
\frac{|00\rangle + i|01\rangle - |10\rangle - i|11\rangle}{\sqrt{4}} \tag{7.34}
$$

Next we need to apply a closing hadamard gate to q_1:

$$
\frac{1}{\sqrt{2}} \begin{bmatrix} 1 & 0 & 1 & 0 \\ 0 & 1 & 0 & 1 \\ 1 & 0 & -1 & 0 \\ 0 & 1 & 0 & -1 \end{bmatrix} \frac{1}{\sqrt{4}} \begin{bmatrix} 1 \\ i \\ -1 \\ -i \end{bmatrix} \tag{7.35}
$$

$$
= \frac{1}{\sqrt{2}} \begin{bmatrix} 1(1) + 0(i) + 1(-1) + 0(-i) \\ 0(1) + 1(i) + 0(-1) + 1(-i) \\ 1(1) + 0(i) + -1(-1) + 0(-i) \\ 0(1) + 1(i) + 0(-1) + -1(-i) \end{bmatrix} = \frac{1}{\sqrt{2}} \begin{bmatrix} 0 \\ 0 \\ 1 \\ i \end{bmatrix} \tag{7.36}
$$

Next we need to reapply the CU gate to q_1. Note that when we applied the CU gate in the original QFT we set the rotation amount to $\frac{\pi}{2}$. As such in the inverse QFT we do an inverse rotation of $-\frac{\pi}{2}$

$$
\begin{bmatrix} 1 & 0 & 0 & 0 \\ 0 & 1 & 0 & 0 \\ 0 & 0 & 1 & 0 \\ 0 & 0 & 0 & e^{i\left(-\frac{\pi}{2}\right)} \end{bmatrix} \frac{1}{\sqrt{2}} \begin{bmatrix} 0 \\ 0 \\ 1 \\ i \end{bmatrix} \tag{7.37}
$$

$$
= \frac{1}{\sqrt{2}} \begin{bmatrix} 1(0) + 0(0) + 0(1) + 0(i) \\ 0(0) + 1(0) + 0(1) + 0(i) \\ 0(0) + 0(0) + 1(1) + 0(i) \\ 0(0) + 0(0) + 0(1) + e^{i\left(-\frac{\pi}{2}\right)}(i) \end{bmatrix} = \frac{1}{\sqrt{2}} \begin{bmatrix} 0 \\ 0 \\ 1 \\ 1 \end{bmatrix} \tag{7.38}
$$

Finally if apply the closing hadamard gate to q_0 we will get back our original state which was $|10\rangle$!

7.7 Shor's Algorithm

Alongside Grover's algorithm Shor's algorithm is one of the best known examples of a quantum algorithm that has a clear advantage over any classical equivalent. Discovered by Peter Shor in 1994 this algorithm makes use of quantum mechanical phenomenon to speed up factoring of integers. Factoring may seem trivial but it has profound implications as various cryptographic methods such as RSA rely on the use of prime numbers and keeping those numbers secret. In essence this algorithm could make classical encryption useless overnight once we have quantum computers with enough computational power.

Shor's algorithm works by reducing the problem of factoring to order finding and then using a quantum computer to solve the order-finding problem using the Quantum Fourier Transform (QFT).

The algorithm is divided in to the following steps:

1. Pick a number a between 1 and N where N is the number we wish to factor

2. Find the Greatest Common Divisor (GCD) of a and N

3. If the GCD is found and is not 1 then we have successfully factored N!

4. If we have not found the GCD then we use a quantum circuit to find the period (r) of the following function:

$$f(x) = a^x mod N \qquad (7.39)$$

5. If r is even then use the Euclidean algorithm to compute $gcd(a^{r/2} + 1, N)$ and $gcd(a^{r/2} - 1, N)$. If successful then we have successfully factored N!

From the steps we can see that quantum computing is used in the algorithm to find the period (r) of $f(x) = a^x mod N$. The period r also has to be the smallest integer such that:

$$a^r mod N = 1 \tag{7.40}$$

If we can find this period then we can use that to find $gcd(a^{r/2} + 1, N)$ and $gcd(a^{r/2} - 1, N)$ which should correspond to the two prime factors. The period r is found using the quantum circuit below. The circuit consists of two registers:

1. An input register that applies unitary operators to the second register

2. A second register that has a set of applied unitary rotations set to it

In the circuit the input register is put in to superposition like so:

$$\frac{1}{\sqrt{k}} \sum_{x=0}^{k-1} |x\rangle \tag{7.41}$$

Where k is the number of possible states. Rule of thumb is the number of states $= 2^i$ where i is the number of qubits. For example if we had 8 qubits then we would have 2^8 which equals 256 possible states when in superposition.

Next we apply unitary rotations to the second register. Due to phase kickback this will encode r in to the input qubits!

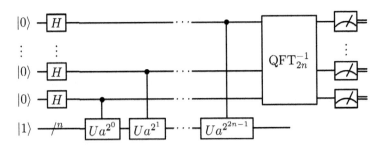

Figure 7.19: Circuit used to find the period r

Then in order to get r out of the phase of the input register we need to apply an inverse quantum fourier transform and measure the qubits.

7.8 Quantum Phase Estimation

Phase estimation is an important algorithm that estimates the phase unitary operator. More specifically given the unitary operator O and a quantum state $|\psi\rangle$ the phase estimation algorithm will estimate the value of θ in $O|\psi\rangle e^{2\pi i \theta}$

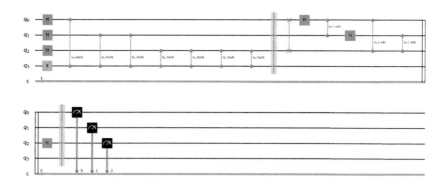

Figure 7.20: Circuit diagram of phase estimation circuit

The algorithm is essentially just a quantum circuit consisting of counting qubits and the qubit whose phase we wish to estimate $|\psi\rangle$. The algorithm consists of the following steps:

- Put the counting qubits in to superposition using hadamard gates

- Apply controlled unitary operations that rotate the phase by θ

- Apply the inverse Quantum Fourier Transform

113

- Measure the counting qubits

After the qubits are measured the phase θ is estimated by taking the measured value M such that:

$$\theta = \frac{M}{2^n} \tag{7.42}$$

where n is the number of counting qubits.

For example if the measured value is 011 then we convert it to its integer value which is 3 such that:

$$\frac{3}{2^n} = 0.375 \tag{7.43}$$

As such the approximate value of $\theta = 0.375$

7.9 Grover's Algorithm

Grover's algorithm is one of the most well known quantum algorithms as like Shor's algorithm it demonstrates a clear advantage over classical algorithms. Also known as Grover's search algorithm it uses quantum mechanics to find the input x to a function $f(x)$ such that the function will give out a specific output ie $f(x) = 1$.

Grover's algorithm is usually described as an algorithm for database search. However it has many more uses that just for searching unstructured databases. While a classical algorithm may in a worse case scenario find the input in $O(n)$ Grover's instead can find the input in only $O\sqrt{(n)}$ queries. The algorithm works by putting all qubits in to superposition and then essentially amplifying the amplitude of the good states while decreasing the amplitude of any bad states. Thus when the qubits are measured the output should correspond to what we wish to find.

The basic steps for the algorithm are as such:

1. Put all qubits in to superposition using hadamard gates

2. Apply an oracle to invert the amplitude of the good states

3. Apply a diffusion operator to amplify the amplitude of the good states while reducing the amplitude of the bad states

8 Quantum Error Correction

Current superconducting qubits are very fragile and are prone to decoherence due to environmental noise such as temperature or stray magnetic fields. As such there has been a big push to develop quantum error correction schemes. Quantum error correction is any method whereby qubit errors are actively corrected. This is done by applying a quantum circuit that corrects an error on a logical qubit using auxiliary qubits.

There are two main types of quantum error:

1. Bit flips where the state of a qubit flips from $|0\rangle$ to $|1\rangle$ or vice versa

2. Phase flips which flip the phase of a qubit from $|-\rangle$ to $|+\rangle$ or vice versa

Bit flips can be corrected using a circuit called the bit flip code while phase flips can be corrected using the phase flip code. Both error types can also be corrected using the Shor code.

8.1 Bit Flip code

The bit flip code is a quantum circuit used to correct bit flips. It uses two auxiliary qubits to correct one logical qubit denoted in the figure below as $|\psi\rangle$. The circuit is very simple as it only consists of CNOT gates and a Toffoli gate. In the figure below the bit flip (denoted as Ebit) is seen as acting on all the qubits. The reason why is even though the circuit is used to correct $|\psi\rangle$ a bit flip can happen to any of the qubits.

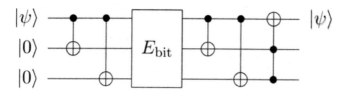

Figure 8.1: Circuit diagram of the bit flip circuit

So how does the circuit work? Well first the auxiliary qubits (which we will call q_1 and q_2) are initialised to $|0\rangle$. Next the state of the main qubit which we will call q_0 is transferred to q_1 and q_2 using CNOT gates. Next a bit flip may occur which flips the state of q_0 from $|0\rangle$ to $|1\rangle$ or vice versa. Next the CNOT gates are again applied to q_1 and q_2 where q_0 is the control qubit. Next the error is corrected by flipping the state of $q0$ using a toffoli gate where q_1 and q_2 are the control qubits.

For our first example let's set q_0 to $|0\rangle$. The overall state of the system will be $|000\rangle$ and as such the column vector will be:

$$|000\rangle = \begin{bmatrix} 1 \\ 0 \\ 0 \\ 0 \\ 0 \\ 0 \\ 0 \\ 0 \end{bmatrix} \tag{8.1}$$

Next a CNOT gates is applied to q_1 and q_2 where q_0 is the control. Since the main qubits state is $|0\rangle$ the state of the system will remain $|000\rangle$. Next a bit flip will affect the main qubit, It is important to note that a bit flip is essentially an unwanted Pauli-X gate applied to the main qubit. This will flip the main qubit to $|1\rangle$ and as such the overll state of the system will be:

$$|001\rangle = \begin{bmatrix} 0 \\ 1 \\ 0 \\ 0 \\ 0 \\ 0 \\ 0 \\ 0 \end{bmatrix} \tag{8.2}$$

So now that the main qubit has an error it is time to correct it. This is done by first reapplying CNOT gates to q_1 and q_2. This will flip their states to $|1\rangle$ such that the overall state will become:

$$|111\rangle = \begin{bmatrix} 0 \\ 0 \\ 0 \\ 0 \\ 0 \\ 0 \\ 0 \\ 1 \end{bmatrix} \hspace{3cm} (8.3)$$

Next a toffoli gate is applied to q_0 where q_1 and q_2 are the control qubits. Since both q_1 and q_2 are $|1\rangle$ this will flip q_0 back to $|0\rangle$ and correct the error!

8.2 Phase Flip code

The phase flip code is an error correction circuit used to correct a type of error called a phase flip. A phase flip is an error that flips the phase of the qubit from $|+\rangle$ to $|-\rangle$ or vice versa. The circuits similar to the bit flip circuit in that it consists of a logical qubit that we wish to correct and two auxiliary qubits. It also makes use of CNOT gates and toffoli gates in the same way as the bit flip circuit but differs in that it puts the qubits in to superposition before an error occurs and then brings the qubits out of superposition after the error has occurred.

The circuit works by first initialising q_1 and q_2 to $|0\rangle$. Then a CNOT gate is applied to q_1 and q_2 where q_0 is the control. Next all qubits are put in to superposition. Then a phase flip error will occur and flip the phase of the main qubit from $|+\rangle$ to $|-\rangle$ or vice versa. Then all qubits are brought out of superposition.

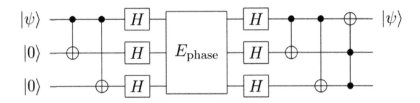

Figure 8.2: Circuit diagram of the phase flip circuit

Next CNOT gates are again applied to q_1 and q_2 where q_0 is the control. Then finally a toffoli gate is used to correct the state of q_0.

Now lets explore how the phase flip code actually corrects phase flips. For our example lets set q_0 to $|0\rangle$. The first step is to initialise q_1 and q_2 to $|0\rangle$. Overall the state of the system will be $|000\rangle$. Next we apply CNOT gates to q_1 and q_2. Since q_0 is $|0\rangle$ the states of q_1 and q_2 will remain unchanged. Next all qubits are put in to superposition using hadamard gates. This will change the overall state of the system to:

$$\frac{|000\rangle + |001\rangle + |010\rangle... + |111\rangle}{\sqrt{8}} = \frac{1}{\sqrt{8}}\begin{bmatrix} 1 \\ 1 \\ 1 \\ 1 \\ 1 \\ 1 \\ 1 \\ 1 \end{bmatrix} \tag{8.4}$$

Next a phase flip occurs to q_0 which will flip the phase from $|+\rangle$ to $|-\rangle$. It is important to note that a phase flip is essentially an unwanted Pauli-Z gate acting on the qubits state. This phase flip will alter the overall state such:

$$\frac{|000\rangle - |001\rangle + |010\rangle... - |111\rangle}{\sqrt{8}} = \frac{1}{\sqrt{8}}\begin{bmatrix} 1 \\ -1 \\ 1 \\ -1 \\ 1 \\ -1 \\ 1 \\ -1 \end{bmatrix} \quad (8.5)$$

Next the qubits are brought out of superposition. Because the phase of q_0 was flipped from $|+\rangle$ to $|-\rangle$ this will set its state to $|1\rangle$ whereas if no error occurred it would of been $|0\rangle$. This is because the phase of the qubit affects the state of the qubit in the computational basis once it is brought out of superposition.

$$\frac{|0\rangle - |1\rangle}{\sqrt{2}} \longrightarrow |1\rangle \quad (8.6)$$

The overall state of the system will be:

$$|001\rangle = \begin{bmatrix} 0 \\ 1 \\ 0 \\ 0 \\ 0 \\ 0 \\ 0 \\ 0 \end{bmatrix} \quad (8.7)$$

Next CNOT gates are again applied to q_1 and q_2 where q_0 is the control. Because q_0 is $|1\rangle$ the states of q_1 and q_2 will be flipped to $|1\rangle$ too. The overall state of the system will be:

$$|111\rangle = \begin{bmatrix} 0 \\ 0 \\ 0 \\ 0 \\ 0 \\ 0 \\ 0 \\ 1 \end{bmatrix} \qquad (8.8)$$

Finally a toffoli gate is applied to q_0 where q_1 and q_2 are the control. This will flip the state of q_0 from $|1\rangle$ to $|0\rangle$. As such the error has been corrected!

8.3 Shor code

The bit flip code can correct bit flips but it cannot correct phase flips. The shor code however can correct both bit flips and phase flips. The circuit consist of one main logical qubit that we wish to correct and 8 auxiliary qubits.

The circuit works by first initialising all auxiliary qubits to $|0\rangle$. Next CNOT gates are applied to q_3 and q_6 where q_0 is the control qubit. Next q_0, q_3 and q_6 are put in superposition. Then CNOT gates are applied to q_1, q_2, q_4, q_5, q_7 and q_8. Next a bit flip or phase flip may occur. After this CNOT gates are then applied to the qubits as previous. Then q_0, q_3 and q_6 are taken out of superposition. Then CNOT gates are applied to q_3 and q_6 where q_0 is the control. Finally a toffoli gate is applied to q_0 where q_3 and q_6 are the control qubits. After this the error should be corrected for $|0\rangle$!

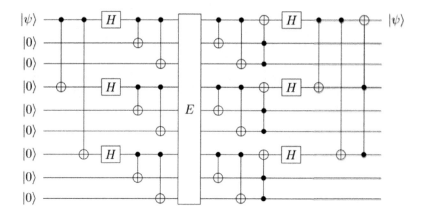

Figure 8.3: Circuit diagram of the shor code circuit

9 Quantum Error Mitigation

While quantum error correction aims to actively correct qubits it has some drawbacks as it usually requires auxiliary qubits in order to perform the correction. Quantum error mitigation however is a more passive approach that aims to reduce the probabilities of errors happening in the first place but does not actively correct the errors.

One example of a mitigation scheme is to map the logical qubits in a circuit to the physical qubits on a device which have the lowest error rates. This is possible as error rates can be different for each qubit even on the same device. Furthermore the qubits can have different error rates for different error types.

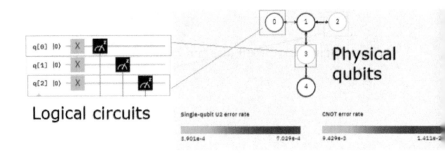

Figure 9.1: Mapping logical qubits in a circuit to the physical qubits on a device with the least error

124

This scheme is surprisingly effective and in a study that I co-authored we found that on some devices error rates can be reduced by up to 35.52% on certain quantum devices [13]. However it was also seen that the method provides minimal performance increase if variance between qubit error rates is low. As such this method is recommended to be used on devices where variance between qubit error rates is high.

Another example of a quantum error mitigation scheme is one by Matthew Otten and Stephen K. Gray. In their scheme noise free observables were recovered from noisy quantum systems by running the same operations on multiple systems [15]. Their scheme did not require use of auxiliary qubits. Instead the only overhead were the repeated measurements required to get the observables. A scheme developed by Xin Zhang et al for circuit optimization involves using a software algorithm to exchange qubits based upon the layout of the device by using SWAP gates [18]. The scheme also further optimized the circuits by merging single qubit gates when necessary and as such reduces the probability of errors. This optimization reduces the probability of errors as the more gates used in a quantum circuit the more opportunity there is for an error to arise when each gate is implemented.

10 Quantum Hardware

So far we have gone through how quantum computing works using circuits made up of qubits and quantum logic gates. However how are the qubits in a superconducting quantum computer actually implemented?

10.1 Superconducting Qubits

A superconducting qubit is a type of qubit that uses a superconducting metal that is cooled to very low temperatures (typically below 100mK). There are 3 main types of superconducting qubits:

10.1.1 Flux Qubit

This type of qubit that makes use of a bias magnetic flux which is induced by a current. It consists of loops of superconducting material that are coupled to Josephon Junctions. States $|0\rangle$ and $|1\rangle$ correspond to the direction of the current (clockwise of anticlockwise) in the superconducting loop. In the diagram below the bias flux is denoted as ϕ and controlled by the current I_0 and the Josephon Junction as E_j. L is the inductance of the superconducting loop.

The Hamiltonian associated with flux qubit is defined as:

$$H = \frac{q^2}{2C_j} + \left(\frac{\Phi_0}{2\pi}\right)^2 \frac{\phi^2}{2L} - E_j cos \left[\phi - \Phi\frac{2\pi}{\Phi_0}\right] \qquad (10.1)$$

where C_J is the capacitance of the Josephon junction and q is the charge. Φ is the bias flux.

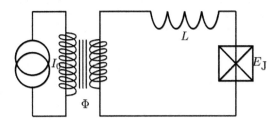

Figure 10.1: Circuit diagram of the Flux Qubit

10.1.2 Charge Qubit

A charge qubit makes use of a superconducting island between a capacitor and a Josephon Junction. A cooper pair is a pair of electrons that are bound together at low temperatures and hence the qubit has to be cooled to very low temperatures. In the diagram below C is the capacitor while E_J is the Josephon Junction and U is the bias voltage. The states of the qubit $|0\rangle$ and $|1\rangle$ are determined by the number of cooper pairs within the island. Charge qubits are a very popular type of qubit as they are used by such companies as IBM and Google. However they tend to be prone to noise and thus prone to error.

The Hamiltonian for the flux qubit is defined as:

$$H = E_C(N - N_g)^2 - E_J cos\phi \qquad (10.2)$$

Where where N is the number of Cooper pairs that tunnel through the Josephon junction and N_g is the charge on the capacitor. E_C is the energy associated with the capacitance and the josephon junction capacitance.

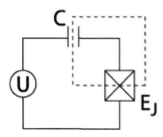

Figure 10.2: Circuit diagram of the Charge Qubit

10.1.3 Phase Qubit

A Phase qubit is similar to a flux qubit or charge qubit in that it makes use of a Josephon Junction. However the main difference is that it is biased by a bias current.

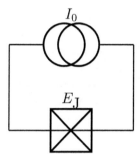

Figure 10.3: Circuit diagram of the Phase Qubit

The Hamiltonian for the phase qubit is:

$$H = \frac{(2e)^2}{2C_J}q^2 - I_0\frac{\Phi_0}{2\pi} - E_J cos\phi \tag{10.3}$$

where E_J is the energy across the Josephon junction and C_J is the capacitance across it. q is the charge and Φ is the magnetic flux quantity.

11 Qiskit: Getting Started

11.1 What is Qiskit?

Qiskit is an open source software development kit for working with IBM quantum devices. It allows users to create quantum programs which can be sent off as jobs to IBM's quantum devices or simulated on local machines. The Qiskit framework is divided in to four main libraries

- Qiskit Aer

- Qiskit Terra

- Qiskit Ignis

- Qiskit Aqua

11.2 Installing Qiskit

Since Qiskit is a Python library you will require Python 3.X and can be installed directly using the pip python package management system. In order to install Qiskit and its dependencies simply open up Command Prompt and type in the line below:

```
pip install qiskit
```

You can check if Qiskit has installed successfully by typing **pip list**. This will list all the packages installed. If Qiskit has installed successfully you should se the following packges has been installed:

- qiskit

- qiskit-aer

- qiskit-aqua

- qiskit-ignis

- qiskit-terra

Now that we have Qiskit up and running we can start programming!

11.3 Qiskit: Our first program

For our first program we will start simply by creating a quantum circuit consisting of 1 qubit. We will then apply a Pauli X gate and measure the qubit.

11.3.1 Step 1: Import the appropriate libraries

The first step we need to do is to import the appropriate libraries and classes that our program will need. The following will be used:

- QuantumRegister: This is the main class for creating a quantum register in Qiskit. Remember that a quantum register is simply a set of qubits

- ClassicalRegister: This is the main class for creating a classical register. To measure a qubit in Qiskit you have to pass the qubit measurement to a classical register.

- QuantumCircuit: This is the main class for creating a quantum circuit in qiskit.

- execute: This is used to execute quantum circuits on a backend device

- IBMQ: This is the module for the IBMQ providers

- job_monitor: This allows us to monitor the job while it is executed on a backend device

To import all these we just type in the code below:

```
from qiskit import QuantumRegister, ClassicalRegister,
    QuantumCircuit, execute,IBMQ
from qiskit.tools.monitor import job_monitor
```

11.3.2 Step 2: Setup the IBMQ account

The next step is to setup your IBMQ account. This will allow you to access IBM's backend quantum devices. In order to do this you will need to setup an account here on the IBM Quantum site: **https://quantum-computing.ibm.com** After this head over to your account details at **https://quantum-computing.ibm.com/account** and copy your API token.

After you have copy and pasted the API token pass it in to the following code below:

```
IBMQ.enable_account('ENTER API KEY HERE')
```

11.3.3 Step 3: Initialise the provider and backend

Next we have to specify the provider and backend device using the code below:

```
provider = IBMQ.get_provider(hub='ibm-q')
backend = provider.get_backend('ibmq_qasm_simulator')
```

Note that **ibmq_qasm_simulator** is a backend simulator. Throughout the qiskit chapters this backend will be used as it executes jobs very quickly. The actual quantum devices tend to have a longer queue and as such longer execution times for each job. Qiskit also has a set of quantum simulators that you can run on your local machine which we will explore later.

11.3.4 Step 4: Initialise registers and quantum circuit

The next step now is to initialise the quantum and classical registers as well as the quantum circuit. The quantum register is the collection of qubits within the circuit while the classical register are the list of bits used when measuring the qubits. The quantum register can be initialised using the following line of code:

```
q = QuantumRegister(number_of_qubits,'q')
```

Where number_of_qubits is the number of qubits we want in the register. For example if we wanted 2 qubits the code would be:

```
q = QuantumRegister(2,'q')
```

For the classical register we can initialise it much like the quantum register with the following code:

```
c = ClassicalRegister(number_of_bits,'c')
```

Where number_of_bits is the number of classical bits we want to add to the register. For example if we wanted to add 2 bits to the classical register we would use the following code:

```
c = ClassicalRegister(2,'c')
```

To initialise the quantum register we use the following code:

```
circuit = QuantumCircuit(q,c)
```

Where q and c are the quantum and classical registers that are part of the circuit.

11.3.5 Step 5: Build the Quantum circuit

The next step is to build the quantum circuit. Remember that our circuit will apply a Pauli X gate to 1 qubit and then we will measure that qubit.

To build the circuit we add the following code:

```
circuit.x(q[0])
circuit.measure(q,c)
```

circuit.x(q[0]) applies a Pauli X gate to qubit 0 and circuit.measure(q,c) measures all the qubits in the circuit.

11.3.6 Step 6: Execute the circuit on the back end device

In order to execute the circuit on the backend device we use the fallowing code:

```
job = execute(circuit, backend, shots=1)
job_monitor(job)
```

Where circuit is the circuit we initialised earlier and the backend is the backend device. In our case this is the IBMQ qasm simulator. The shots are the number of times we want to run the circuit on the device before returning the results. In our case we leave the number of shots to 1. The job_monitor(job) function allows us to monitor the job in case an error occurs or the job fails for whatever reason.

11.3.7 Step 7: Obtain the results

The last step is to get the results and print them. This can be done in only 2 lines of code:

```
counts = job.result().get_counts()
print(counts)
```

Where job.result().get_counts() obtains the number of counts. The counts are measurements from each qubit in the computational basis ie $|0\rangle$ or $|1\rangle$. Now that we have gone through each line of code in detail lets see the full code below.

11.3.8 Code

```
from qiskit import QuantumRegister, ClassicalRegister
from qiskit import QuantumCircuit, execute,IBMQ
from qiskit.tools.monitor import job_monitor

IBMQ.enable_account('Enter API KEY HERE')
provider = IBMQ.get_provider(hub='ibm-q')

backend = provider.get_backend('ibmq_qasm_simulator')

q = QuantumRegister(1,'q')
c = ClassicalRegister(1,'c')

circuit = QuantumCircuit(q,c)

circuit.x(q[0])
circuit.measure(q,c)

print(circuit)

job = execute(circuit, backend, shots=1)

job_monitor(job)
counts = job.result().get_counts()

print(counts)
```

12 Qiskit: Hadamard Gate

This program creates a circuit consisting of 1 qubit. Once initialised a Hadamard (H) operation is applied to the qubit effectively putting it in to a superposition of states such that if the qubit is $|0\rangle$ then the state will become:

$$|0\rangle \longrightarrow \frac{|0\rangle + |1\rangle}{\sqrt{2}} \tag{12.1}$$

and if it was $|1\rangle$ then the state will become:

$$|1\rangle \longrightarrow \frac{|0\rangle - |1\rangle}{\sqrt{2}} \tag{12.2}$$

The Hadamard gate is described using the following matrix:

$$H = \frac{1}{\sqrt{2}} \begin{bmatrix} 1 & 1 \\ 1 & -1 \end{bmatrix}$$

12.0.1 Code

```
from qiskit import QuantumRegister, ClassicalRegister,
    QuantumCircuit, execute, IBMQ
from qiskit.tools.monitor import job_monitor

IBMQ.enable_account('Insert account token here') # Get
    this from your IBM Q account
provider = IBMQ.get_provider(hub='ibm-q')
```

137

```
q = QuantumRegister(1,'q') # Initialise quantum register
c = ClassicalRegister(1,'c') # Initialise classical
    register

circuit = QuantumCircuit(q,c) # Initialise circuit
circuit.h(q[0]) # Put Qubit 0 in to superposition using
    hadamard gate
circuit.measure(q,c) # Measure qubit

backend = provider.get_backend('ibmq_qasm_simulator') #
    Set device to IBMs quantum simulator
job = execute(circuit, backend, shots=1024) # Execute job
    and run program 1024 times

job_monitor(job)
counts = job.result().get_counts()

print('RESULT: ',counts) # Print result
print('Press any key to close')
input()
```

13 Qiskit: Pauli X Gate

The Pauli X gate is a gate that does a rotation around the X-axis by 180 degrees (π radians)

The matrix for the X gate is:

$$X = \begin{bmatrix} 0 & 1 \\ 1 & 0 \end{bmatrix} \tag{13.1}$$

Using matrix multiplication we can see how the X gate operates on the qubits state. For our first example lets initialise the qubits state to $|0\rangle$ and multiply the column vector by the Pauli x matrix:

$$\begin{bmatrix} 0 & 1 \\ 1 & 0 \end{bmatrix} \begin{bmatrix} 1 \\ 0 \end{bmatrix} = \begin{bmatrix} 0(1) + 1(0) \\ 1(1) + 0(0) \end{bmatrix} = \begin{bmatrix} 0 \\ 1 \end{bmatrix} = |1\rangle \tag{13.2}$$

Which has transformed the state from $|0\rangle$ to $|1\rangle$. If we instead intialise the qubit to $|1\rangle$

$$\begin{bmatrix} 0 & 1 \\ 1 & 0 \end{bmatrix} \begin{bmatrix} 0 \\ 1 \end{bmatrix} = \begin{bmatrix} 0(0) + 1(1) \\ 1(0) + 0(1) \end{bmatrix} = \begin{bmatrix} 1 \\ 0 \end{bmatrix} = |0\rangle \tag{13.3}$$

Which has flipped the qubit from $|1\rangle$ to $|0\rangle$

13.0.1 Implementation

In Qiskit we can implement an X gate very easily using the following function:

```
circuit.x(q[0])
```

13.0.2 How to run the program

1. Copy and paste the code below in to a python file

2. Enter your API token in the IBMQ.enable_account('Insert API token here') part

3. Save and run

13.0.3 Code

```
from qiskit import QuantumRegister, ClassicalRegister
from qiskit import QuantumCircuit, execute,IBMQ
from qiskit.tools.monitor import job_monitor

IBMQ.enable_account('ENTER API KEY HERE')
provider = IBMQ.get_provider(hub='ibm-q')

backend = provider.get_backend('ibmq_qasm_simulator')


q = QuantumRegister(1,'q')
c = ClassicalRegister(1,'c')

circuit = QuantumCircuit(q,c)
```

```
circuit.x(q[0])
circuit.measure(q,c)

print(circuit)

job = execute(circuit, backend, shots=8192)
job_monitor(job)
counts = job.result().get_counts()
print(counts)
```

14 Qiskit: Pauli Y Gate

The Pauli Y gate is a gate that does a rotation around the Y-axis by 180 degrees (π radians)

The matrix for the Y gate is:

$$Y = \begin{bmatrix} 0 & -i \\ i & 0 \end{bmatrix} \tag{14.1}$$

Using matrix multiplication we can see how the Y gate operates on the qubits state. For our first example lets initialise the qubits state to $|0\rangle$ and multiply the column vector by the Pauli Y matrix:

$$\begin{bmatrix} 0 & -i \\ i & 0 \end{bmatrix} \begin{bmatrix} 1 \\ 0 \end{bmatrix} = \begin{bmatrix} 0(1) + -i(0) \\ i(1) + 0(0) \end{bmatrix} = \begin{bmatrix} 0 \\ i \end{bmatrix} \tag{14.2}$$

which is correct as the resulting column vector is for $i|1\rangle$. If we instead initialise the qubit to $|1\rangle$:

$$\begin{bmatrix} 0 & -i \\ i & 0 \end{bmatrix} \begin{bmatrix} 0 \\ 1 \end{bmatrix} = \begin{bmatrix} 0(0) + -i(1) \\ i(0) + 0(1) \end{bmatrix} = \begin{bmatrix} -i \\ 0 \end{bmatrix} \tag{14.3}$$

Which is correct as the column vector is for $-i|0\rangle$

14.0.1 Implementation

In Qiskit we can implement a Y gate very easily using the following function:

```
circuit.y(q[0])
```

14.0.2 How to run the program

1. Copy and paste the code below in to a python file

2. Enter your API token in the IBMQ.enable_account('Insert API token here') part

3. Save and run

14.0.3 Code

```
from qiskit import QuantumRegister, ClassicalRegister
from qiskit import QuantumCircuit, execute,IBMQ
from qiskit.tools.monitor import job_monitor

IBMQ.enable_account('ENTER API KEY HERE')
provider = IBMQ.get_provider(hub='ibm-q')

backend = provider.get_backend('ibmq_qasm_simulator')

q = QuantumRegister(1,'q')
c = ClassicalRegister(1,'c')

circuit = QuantumCircuit(q,c)

circuit.y(q[0])
```

```
circuit.measure(q,c)

print(circuit)

job = execute(circuit, backend, shots=8192)
job_monitor(job)
counts = job.result().get_counts()
print(counts)
```

15 Qiskit: Pauli Z Gate

The Pauli Z gate is a gate that does a rotation around the Z-axis by 180 degrees (π radians)

The matrix for the Z gate is:

$$Z = \begin{bmatrix} 1 & 0 \\ 0 & -1 \end{bmatrix} \tag{15.1}$$

Using matrix multiplication we can see how the Z gate operates on the qubits state. For our first example lets initialise the qubits state to $|0\rangle$ and multiply the column vector by the Pauli Z matrix:

$$\begin{bmatrix} 1 & 0 \\ 0 & -1 \end{bmatrix} \begin{bmatrix} 1 \\ 0 \end{bmatrix} = \begin{bmatrix} 1(1) + 0(0) \\ 0(1) + -1(0) \end{bmatrix} = \begin{bmatrix} 1 \\ 0 \end{bmatrix} \tag{15.2}$$

Which is correct as it has left $|0\rangle$ unchanged. Now let's initialise the qubit to $|1\rangle$ and see how the Z gate transforms the qubits state:

$$\begin{bmatrix} 1 & 0 \\ 0 & -1 \end{bmatrix} \begin{bmatrix} 0 \\ 1 \end{bmatrix} = \begin{bmatrix} 1(0) + 0(1) \\ 0(0) + -1(1) \end{bmatrix} = \begin{bmatrix} 0 \\ -1 \end{bmatrix} \tag{15.3}$$

Which is correct as it has changed the qubits state from $|1\rangle$ to $-|1\rangle$

15.0.1 Implementation

In Qiskit we can implement a Z gate very easily using the following function:

```
circuit.z(q[0])
```

15.0.2 How to run the program

1. Copy and paste the code below in to a python file

2. Enter your API token in the IBMQ.enable_account('Insert API token here') part

3. Save and run

15.0.3 Code

```
from qiskit import QuantumRegister, ClassicalRegister
from qiskit import QuantumCircuit, execute,IBMQ
from qiskit.tools.monitor import job_monitor

IBMQ.enable_account('ENTER API KEY HERE')
provider = IBMQ.get_provider(hub='ibm-q')

backend = provider.get_backend('ibmq_qasm_simulator')

q = QuantumRegister(1,'q')
c = ClassicalRegister(1,'c')

circuit = QuantumCircuit(q,c)

circuit.z(q[0])
```

```
circuit.measure(q,c)

print(circuit)

job = execute(circuit, backend, shots=8192)
job_monitor(job)
counts = job.result().get_counts()
print(counts)
```

16 Qiskit RX Gate

The RX gate is a gate that does a rotation around the X-axis by a specified angle which is normally denoted by θ.

The matrix for the RX gate is:

$$RX = \begin{bmatrix} \cos\frac{\theta}{2} & -\sin\frac{\theta}{2} \\ -\sin\frac{\theta}{2} & \cos\frac{\theta}{2} \end{bmatrix} \tag{16.1}$$

Using matrix multiplication we can see how the RX gate operates on the qubits state. For our first example lets initialise the qubits state to $|0\rangle$ and set θ to be π. Then we multiply the associated column vector for $|0\rangle$ with the RX matrix. This should flip the qubits state from $|0\rangle$ to $|1\rangle$

16.0.1 Implementation

In Qiskit we can implement an RX gate very easily using the following function:

```
circuit.rx(pi,q[0])
```

Where π is the rotation amount and q[0] is the qubit we want to apply the RX gate to.

16.0.2 How to run the program

1. Copy and paste the code below in to a python file

2. Enter your API token in the IBMQ.enable_account('Insert API token here') part

3. Save and run

16.0.3 Code

```
from qiskit import QuantumRegister, ClassicalRegister
from qiskit import QuantumCircuit, execute,IBMQ
from qiskit.tools.monitor import job_monitor
import numpy as np

IBMQ.enable_account('ENTER API KEY HERE')
provider = IBMQ.get_provider(hub='ibm-q')

backend = provider.get_backend('ibmq_qasm_simulator')

pi = np.pi

q = QuantumRegister(1,'q')
c = ClassicalRegister(1,'c')

circuit = QuantumCircuit(q,c)

circuit.rx(pi,q[0])
circuit.measure(q,c)

print(circuit)

job = execute(circuit, backend, shots=8192)
job_monitor(job)
counts = job.result().get_counts()
print(counts)
```

17 Qiskit: RY Gate

The RY gate is a gate that does a rotation around the Y-axis by a specified angle which is normally denoted by θ.

The matrix for the RY gate is:

$$RY = \begin{bmatrix} \cos\frac{\theta}{2} & -\sin\frac{\theta}{2} \\ \sin\frac{\theta}{2} & \cos\frac{\theta}{2} \end{bmatrix} \qquad (17.1)$$

Using the matrix multiplication we can see how the RY gate operates on the qubits state. For our first example lets initialise the qubits state to $|0\rangle$ and set θ to be π. This should flip the qubits state from $|0\rangle$ to $|1\rangle$.

17.0.1 Implementation

In Qiskit we can implement an RY gate very easily using the following function:

```
circuit.yx(pi,q[0])
```

Where π is the rotation amount and q[0] is the qubit we want to apply the RY gate to.

17.0.2 How to run the program

1. Copy and paste the code below in to a python file

2. Enter your API token in the IBMQ.enable_account('Insert API token here') part

3. Save and run

17.0.3 Code

```
from qiskit import QuantumRegister, ClassicalRegister
from qiskit import QuantumCircuit, execute,IBMQ
from qiskit.tools.monitor import job_monitor
import numpy as np

IBMQ.enable_account('ENTER API KEY HERE')
provider = IBMQ.get_provider(hub='ibm-q')

backend = provider.get_backend('ibmq_qasm_simulator')

pi = np.pi

q = QuantumRegister(1,'q')
c = ClassicalRegister(1,'c')

circuit = QuantumCircuit(q,c)

circuit.ry(pi,q[0])
circuit.measure(q,c)

print(circuit)

job = execute(circuit, backend, shots=8192)
job_monitor(job)
counts = job.result().get_counts()
print(counts)
```

18 Qiskit: RZ Gate

The RZ gate is a gate that does a rotation around the Z-axis by a specified angle which is normally denoted by λ.

The matrix for the RY gate is:

$$RZ = \begin{bmatrix} e^{-i\frac{\lambda}{2}} & 0 \\ 0 & e^{i\frac{\lambda}{2}} \end{bmatrix} \tag{18.1}$$

Using the matrix multiplication we can see how the RZ gate operates on the qubits state. For our first example lets initialise the qubits state to $|0\rangle$ and set λ to be π. This should flip the qubits state from $|0\rangle$ to $|0\rangle$.

18.0.1 Implementation

In Qiskit we can implement an RZ gate very easily using the following function:

```
circuit.rz(pi,q[0])
```

Where π is the rotation amount and q[0] is the qubit we want to apply the RY gate to.

18.0.2 How to run the program

1. Copy and paste the code below in to a python file

2. Enter your API token in the IBMQ.enable_account('Insert API token here') part

3. Save and run

18.0.3 Code

```
from qiskit import QuantumRegister, ClassicalRegister
from qiskit import QuantumCircuit, execute,IBMQ
from qiskit.tools.monitor import job_monitor
import numpy as np

IBMQ.enable_account('ENTER API KEY HERE')
provider = IBMQ.get_provider(hub='ibm-q')

backend = provider.get_backend('ibmq_qasm_simulator')

pi = np.pi

q = QuantumRegister(1,'q')
c = ClassicalRegister(1,'c')

circuit = QuantumCircuit(q,c)

circuit.ry(pi,q[0])
circuit.measure(q,c)

print(circuit)

job = execute(circuit, backend, shots=8192)
job_monitor(job)
counts = job.result().get_counts()
print(counts)
```

19 Qiskit: CNOT Gate

This is a simple program for beginners demonstrating how CNOT gate works.

19.0.1 What it does

This program entangles 2 qubits with a Controlled NOT gate.

1. First 2 qubits are initialised.

2. A Pauli X gate is applied to the first qubit so that its state is $|1\rangle$.

3. Then a CNOT is applied to both gates. Because the first qubit is $|1\rangle$ the second qubit will be flipped to $|1\rangle$.

19.0.2 Code

```
from qiskit import QuantumRegister, ClassicalRegister,
    QuantumCircuit, execute,IBMQ
from qiskit.tools.monitor import job_monitor

IBMQ.enable_account('Enter API token here')
provider = IBMQ.get_provider(hub='ibm-q')

q = QuantumRegister(2,'q')
c = ClassicalRegister(2,'c')
```

```
circuit = QuantumCircuit(q,c)
circuit.x(q[0]) # Pauli x gate applied to first qubit
circuit.cx(q[0],q[1]) # CNOT applied to both qubits
circuit.measure(q,c) # Qubits states are measured

backend = provider.get_backend('ibmq_qasm_simulator') #
    Specifying qasm simulator as the target device

print('Provider: ',backend)
print('')

job = execute(circuit, backend, shots=1)

print('Executing Job...')
print('')
job_monitor(job)
counts = job.result().get_counts()

print('RESULT: ',counts)
print('')
print('Press any key to close')
input()
```

20 Qiskit: CNOT Gate with N control qubits

In this tutorial we will explore how to implement a CNOT gate consisting of N qubits in Qiskit for use on IBM's quantum devices.

20.1 Implementation

A CNOT gate consists of two qubits. The first is known as the control qubit and the second is known as the target qubit. If the control qubit is $|1\rangle$ then the target qubits state will be flipped from $|1\rangle$ to $|0\rangle$ or vice versa. However what if we want to flip a qubits state based on more than $|1\rangle$ control qubit? Well we can use the circuit below!

This consists of 4 control qubits (q0 to q3), 3 auxilary qubits (q4 to q6) and 1 target qubit (q7). When q0 to q3 are $|1\rangle$ the auxilary qubits will be flipped using toffoli gates which in turn will flip the state of the target qubit. After the target qubit is flipped the auxiliary qubits have to be returned back to $|0\rangle$ by again applying toffoli gates.

20.2 How to run the program

1. Copy and paste the code below in to a python file

2. Enter your API token in the IBMQ.enable_account('Insert API token here') part

3. Save and run

20.3 Code

```
from qiskit import QuantumRegister, ClassicalRegister
from qiskit import QuantumCircuit, execute,IBMQ
from qiskit.tools.monitor import job_monitor

IBMQ.enable_account('Enter API key here')
provider = IBMQ.get_provider(hub='ibm-q')

backend = provider.get_backend('ibmq_qasm_simulator')


q = QuantumRegister(8, 'q')
c = ClassicalRegister(1, 'c')

circuit = QuantumCircuit(q, c)

circuit.x(q[0])
circuit.x(q[1])
circuit.x(q[2])
circuit.x(q[3])

circuit.ccx(q[0], q[1], q[4])
circuit.ccx(q[2], q[4], q[5])
circuit.ccx(q[3], q[5], q[6])
```

```
circuit.cx(q[6], q[7])

circuit.ccx(q[3], q[5], q[6])
circuit.ccx(q[2], q[4], q[5])
circuit.ccx(q[0], q[1], q[4])

circuit.measure(q[7], c[0])

job = execute(circuit, backend, shots=100)
job_monitor(job)

counts = job.result().get_counts()

print(circuit)
print(counts)
```

21 Qiskit: MCMT Gate

In this chapter we will explore the MCMT gate and how to implement it on IBM's Quantum Computers in Qiskit.

21.0.1 What is the MCMT gate?

The MCMT (Multiple Control Multiple Target) gate is a generalised gate that allows you to add multiple target and control qubits to a range of gate types.

Currently these include:

- Hadamard gate

- X gate

- Y gate

- Z gate

- T gate

- Diagonal gate

- S gate

- S Diagonal gate

21.1 Implementation

In Qiskit the MCMT gate is extremely easy to implement as it can be appended to an existing circuit using the MCMT() function.

```
MCMT(gate,num_ctrl_qubits, num_target_qubits)
```

Where:

- gate: Is the type of gate you want to implement

- num_ctrl_qubits: The number of control qubits

- num_target_qubits: The number of target qubits

The gate argument must be a string and the following:

- 'h' (or 'ch') for the Hadamard gate type

- 'x' (or 'cx') for the X gate type

- 'y' (or 'cy') for the Y gate type

- 'z' (or 'cz') for the Z gate type

- 't' for the T gate type

- 'tdg' for the T diagonal gate type

- 's' for the S gate type

- 'sdg' for the S diagonal gate type

A full code example is in the code section below which shows you how to implement a controlled Hadamard gate consisting of 4 control qubits and 2 target qubits.

21.2 How to run the program

1. Copy and paste the code below in to a python file

2. Enter your API token in the IBMQ.enable_account('Insert API token here') part

3. Save and run

21.3 Code

```
from qiskit import QuantumRegister, ClassicalRegister
from qiskit.circuit.library import MCMT
from qiskit import QuantumCircuit, execute,IBMQ
from qiskit.tools.monitor import job_monitor
import numpy as np

IBMQ.enable_account('ENTER API KEY HERE')
provider = IBMQ.get_provider(hub='ibm-q')

backend = provider.get_backend('ibmq_qasm_simulator')

pi = np.pi

q = QuantumRegister(6,'q')
c = ClassicalRegister(2,'c')

circuit = QuantumCircuit(q,c)

#### This circuit shows how to implement a controlled
    hadamard gate ####
#### consisting of 4 control qubits and 2 target qubits
    ####
```

```
circuit.x(q[0])
circuit.x(q[1])
circuit.x(q[2])
circuit.x(q[3])

circuit += MCMT('h',4,2, label=None)

circuit.measure(q[4],c[0])
circuit.measure(q[5],c[1])

print(circuit)

job = execute(circuit, backend, shots=8192)

job_monitor(job)
counts = job.result().get_counts()

print(counts)
```

21.4 Output

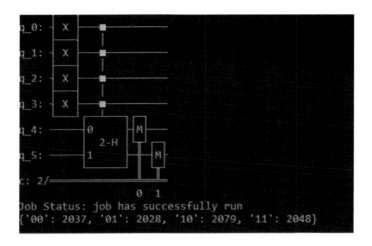

Figure 21.1: Output of the MCMT code

22 Qiskit: Diagonal Gate

The diagonal gate a multi-qubit gate that operates on a qubit based upon diagonal entries in it's matrix. The operation of the diagonal gate can be described using the following matrix:

$$
Diagonal = \begin{bmatrix}
D[0] & 0 & 0 & 0 & \cdots & 0 \\
0 & D[1] & 0 & 0 & \cdots & 0 \\
0 & 0 & D[2] & 0 & \cdots & 0 \\
0 & 0 & 0 & D[3] & \cdots & 0 \\
\vdots & \vdots & \vdots & \vdots & \ddots & 0 \\
0 & 0 & 0 & 0 & \cdots & D[n-1]
\end{bmatrix}
$$

Figure 22.1: Matrix representation of the Diagonal gate

22.0.1 Implementation

In Qiskit the diagonal gate can be implemented very easily using the following function:

```
Diagonal(entries)
```

Where entries is a list of diagonal entries

Note: For K qubits there will be 2^k entries. For example for 2 qubits there will be 4 diagonal entries eg: entries=[-1,1,1,-1]

The diagonal gate is only useful if the qubits are in superposition. In the code below you will notice the qubits have been put in to superposition using Hadamard gates. This is because the diagonal gate operates on the phase of the qubit. Another thing to point out is that the entries can only be an absolute value of 1 that is -1 or +1.

22.0.2 How to run the program

1. Copy and paste the code below in to a python file

2. Enter your API token in the IBMQ.enable_account('Insert API token here') part

3. Save and run

22.0.3 Code

```
from qiskit import QuantumRegister, ClassicalRegister
from qiskit import QuantumCircuit, execute,IBMQ
from qiskit.tools.monitor import job_monitor
from qiskit.circuit.library import Diagonal

pi = np.pi

IBMQ.enable_account('ENTER API KEY HERE')
provider = IBMQ.get_provider(hub='ibm-q')

backend = provider.get_backend('ibmq_qasm_simulator')
```

22 Qiskit: Diagonal Gate

```
diagonals = [-1,1,1,-1]

q = QuantumRegister(2,'q')
c = ClassicalRegister(2,'c')

circuit = QuantumCircuit(q,c)

circuit.h(q[0])
circuit.h(q[1])
circuit += Diagonal(diagonals)
circuit.h(q[0])
circuit.h(q[1])

circuit.measure(q,c) # Qubit Measurment

print(circuit)

job = execute(circuit, backend, shots=8192)

job_monitor(job)

counts = job.result().get_counts()
print(counts)
```

22.0.4 Output

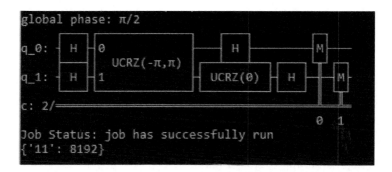

Figure 22.2: Output when running the Diagonal circuit

23 Qiskit: Superdense Coding

Superdense coding is a quantum communications protocol that allows a user to send 2 classical bits by sending only 1 qubit.

23.0.1 The protocol

Step 1: Preparing the Bell pair

First a bell pair consisting of 2 qubits is prepared. Where q_0 is the senders qubit and q_1 is the receivers qubit. To do this q_0 is put in to a superposition of states using a hadamard gate.

Then a CNOT operation is performed with q_0 being the control and q_1 the target.

Step 2: Encode the information on to q_0

Next the sender has to encode the information they want to send on to q0 by applying certain operations to it.

- If they want to send $|00\rangle$ then they perform no operation.

- If they want to send $|01\rangle$ then they perform a Pauli-Z operation where q1s state is flipped.

- If they want to send $|10\rangle$ then they apply a Pauli-X gate.

- If they want to send $|11\rangle$ then apply a Pauli-Z gate followed by a Pauli-X gate

Step 3: Receiver decodes the information

Next q_0 is sent and the receiver has to decode the qubit. This is done by applying a CNOT where the received q_0 is the control and q_1 is the target. Then a hadamard gate is applied to q_0.

23.0.2 How to run the program

1. Copy and paste the code below in to a python file

2. Enter your API token in the IBMQ.enable_account('Insert API token here') part

3. Save and run

23.0.3 Code

```
print('\n Superdense Coding')
print('------------------------\n')

from qiskit import QuantumRegister, ClassicalRegister,
    QuantumCircuit, execute,IBMQ
from qiskit.tools.monitor import job_monitor

IBMQ.enable_account('ENTER API TOKEN')
provider = IBMQ.get_provider(hub='ibm-q')

q = QuantumRegister(2,'q')
c = ClassicalRegister(2,'c')

backend = provider.get_backend('ibmq_qasm_simulator')
print('Provider: ',backend)

################### 00 #########################
```

```
circuit = QuantumCircuit(q,c)

circuit.h(q[0]) # Hadamard gate applied to q0
circuit.cx(q[0],q[1]) # CNOT gate applied
circuit.cx(q[0],q[1])
circuit.h(q[0])

circuit.measure(q,c) # Qubits measured

job = execute(circuit, backend, shots=10)

print('Executing Job...\n')
job_monitor(job)
counts = job.result().get_counts()

print('RESULT: ',counts,'\n')

################### 10 #########################
circuit = QuantumCircuit(q,c)

circuit.h(q[0])
circuit.cx(q[0],q[1])
circuit.x(q[0]) # X-gate applied
circuit.cx(q[0],q[1])
circuit.h(q[0])

circuit.measure(q,c)

job = execute(circuit, backend, shots=10)

print('Executing Job...\n')
job_monitor(job)
counts = job.result().get_counts()

print('RESULT: ',counts,'\n')
```

```
################### 01 ##########################
circuit = QuantumCircuit(q,c)

circuit.h(q[0])
circuit.cx(q[0],q[1])
circuit.z(q[0]) # Z-gate applied to q0
circuit.cx(q[0],q[1])
circuit.h(q[0])

circuit.measure(q,c)

job = execute(circuit, backend, shots=10)

print('Executing Job...\n')
job_monitor(job)
counts = job.result().get_counts()

print('RESULT: ',counts,'\n')

################### 11 ##########################
circuit = QuantumCircuit(q,c)

circuit.h(q[0])
circuit.cx(q[0],q[1])
circuit.z(q[0]) # Z-gate applied
circuit.x(q[0]) # X-gate applied
circuit.cx(q[0],q[1])
circuit.h(q[0])

circuit.measure(q,c)

job = execute(circuit, backend, shots=10)

print('Executing Job...\n')
```

```
job_monitor(job)
counts = job.result().get_counts()

print('RESULT: ',counts,'\n')
print('Press any key to close')
input()
```

23.0.4 Output

After running the code you will see something like the following printed on the screen:

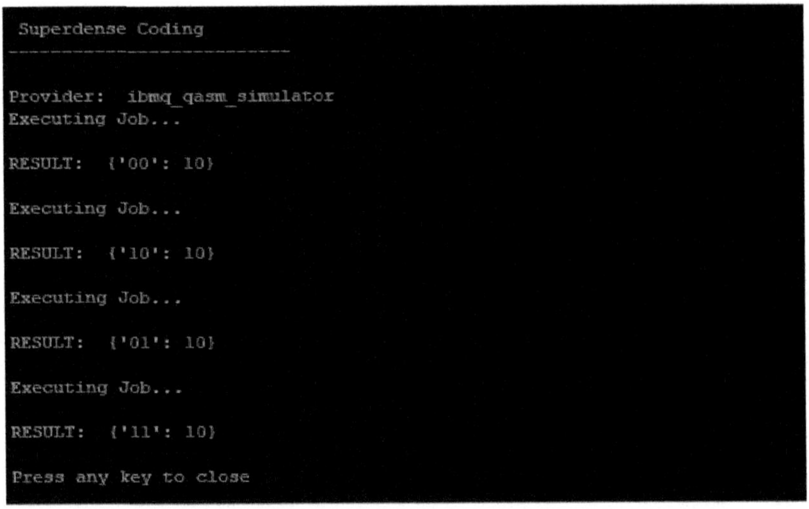

```
Superdense Coding
-------------------------------

Provider:  ibmq_qasm_simulator
Executing Job...

RESULT:  {'00': 10}

Executing Job...

RESULT:  {'10': 10}

Executing Job...

RESULT:  {'01': 10}

Executing Job...

RESULT:  {'11': 10}

Press any key to close
```

Figure 23.1: Superdense code output

24 Qiskit: Random Number Generator

This chapter will show you how to create a random number generator in Qiskit for IBMs quantum computers.

24.0.1 Implementation

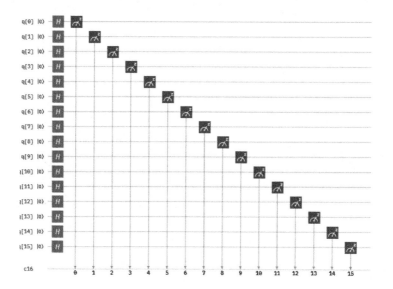

Figure 24.1: Circuit diagram of the random number generator

173

Step 1: Initialise the quantum and classical registers

The first step is to initialise a 16 qubit register. This is done by the following code:

```
q = QuantumRegister(16,'q')
```

Next we initialise the 16 bit classical register with the following code:

```
c = ClassicalRegister(16,'c')
```

Step 2: Create the circuit

Next we create quantum circuit using the following code:

```
circuit = QuantumCircuit(q,c)
```

Step 3: Apply a Hadamard gate to all qubits

Then we need to apply a Hadamard gate. This gate is used to put a qubit in to a superposition of $|1\rangle$ and $|0\rangle$ such that when we measure the qubit it will be $|1\rangle$ or a $|0\rangle$ with equal probability.
This is done with the following code:

```
circuit.h(q)
```

Step 4: Measure the qubits

After this we measure the qubits. This measurement will collapse the qubits superposition in to either a $|1\rangle$ or a $|0\rangle$.

This is done with the following code:

```
circuit.measure(q,c)
```

24.0.2 How to run the program

1. Copy and paste the code below in to a python file

2. Enter your API token in the IBMQ.enable_account('Insert API token here') part

3. Save and run

24.0.3 Code

Here is the code:

```
from qiskit import QuantumRegister, ClassicalRegister,
    QuantumCircuit, execute,IBMQ
from qiskit.tools.monitor import job_monitor

IBMQ.enable_account('ENTER API TOKEN HERE')
provider = IBMQ.get_provider(hub='ibm-q')

q = QuantumRegister(16,'q')
c = ClassicalRegister(16,'c')
circuit = QuantumCircuit(q,c)
circuit.h(q) # Applies hadamard gate to all qubits
circuit.measure(q,c) # Measures all qubits

backend = provider.get_backend('ibmq_qasm_simulator')
job = execute(circuit, backend, shots=1)
```

```
print('Executing Job...\n')
job_monitor(job)
counts = job.result().get_counts()

print('RESULT: ',counts,'\n')
print('Press any key to close')
input()
```

24.0.4 Output

Once you have ran the program you will get the following output:

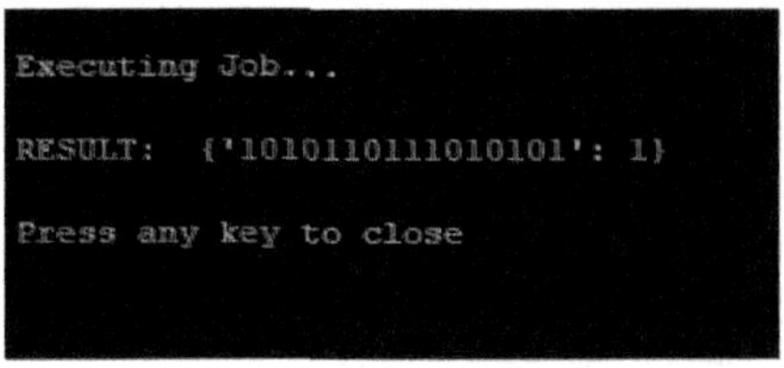

Figure 24.2: Random Number Generator output

25 Qiskit: Shor's Algorithm

In this chapter we will go through and see how to run it on IBM's quantum computers with Python and Qiskit. Shor's Algorithm is a quantum algorithm for integer factorisation. Simply put given an odd integer N it will find it's prime factors.

The algorithm consists of 2 parts:

1. Classical part which reduces the factorisation to a problem of finding the period of the function. This is done classically using a normal computer.

2. Quantum part which uses a quantum computer to find the period using the Quantum Fourier Transform.

For the algorithm the steps are as follows:

1. Pick a random number A such that $A < N$

2. Computer the greatest common divisor (GCD) of and N

3. if the gcd != 1 then we found a factor of N

4. If not then run the quantum circuit that uses a Quantum Fourier Transform

5. If the period is odd then go back to step 1

6. Otherwise we have found the factors of N

25.1 Implementation

The algorithm can be implemented incredibly easily since Qiskit has a baked in function for the algorithm called Shor(N).

Where N will be the integer you wish to factor. For example Shor(21) will find the prime factors for 21.

Note: For this tutorial you will need an API token which you can get by registering here: https://quantum-computing.ibm.com/

25.2 Code

```
rom qiskit import IBMQ
from qiskit.aqua import QuantumInstance
from qiskit.aqua.algorithms import Shor

IBMQ.enable_account('ENTER API TOKEN HERE') # Enter your
    API token here
provider = IBMQ.get_provider(hub='ibm-q')

backend = provider.get_backend('ibmq_qasm_simulator') #
    Specifies the quantum device

print('\n Shors Algorithm')
print('--------------------')
print('\nExecuting...\n')

factors = Shor(21) #Function to run Shor's algorithm where
    21 is the integer to be factored
```

```
result_dict = factors.run(QuantumInstance(backend,
    shots=1, skip_qobj_validation=False))
result = result_dict['factors'] # Get factors from results

print(result)
print('\nPress any key to close')
input()
```

25.3 Output

Figure 25.1: Output for the code above showing the factors 3 and 7 for N=21.

26 Qiskit: Satisfying Logical Expressions using Grover's Search

A logical expression can be defined as an expression made up of a combination of variables that can be true or false. For example consider the following expression:

A AND B

This consists of two variables A, B. The AND operation means that the function will be true if both A,B are true.

A	B	F
0	0	0
0	1	0
1	0	0
1	1	1

Table 26.1: Truth table for AND operation

Where A and B are variables and F is the output.

A OR B

This again consists of two variables A,B. The OR operation means the function will be true if either A or B are true.

A	B	F
0	0	0
0	1	1
1	0	1
1	1	1

Table 26.2: Truth table for OR operation

Where A and B are variables and F is the output.

These expressions can get more complex for example:

(A AND B) OR (C)

This would mean that the function is true if A and B are both true OR C is true. As the number of variables and clauses in-

A	B	C	F
0	0	0	0
0	0	1	1
0	1	0	0
0	1	1	1
1	0	0	0
1	0	1	1
1	1	0	1
1	1	1	1

Table 26.3: Truth table for the expression (A AND B) OR (C)

creases in the expression the more harder it is for a classical computer to evaluate the expression. However using Grover's search algorithm we can find the variable combinations needed that will satisfy the logical expression. Grover's algorithm has a huge advantage over classical methods as the time complexity is only $O(\sqrt{N})$.

26.1 Implementation

Grover's search for logical expressions can be implemented very easily in Qiskit with the following steps:

Step 1: Specify the logical expression

The first step is to specify the logical expression. In Qiskit the logical expression has to be in a specific format where the 'AND' operation is replaced with '&' and the OR operation is replaced with '^' . Negation is done with the '~' character.

For example for the logical expression A AND B we would write:

```
expression = '(a & b)'
```

For the logical expression (A AND B) OR NOT(C):

```
expression = '(a & b)& ~(c)'
```

Step 2: Specify the oracle and pass to the Grover function

The first step is to specify the correct oracle. Since we are evaluating logical expressions you will need to use the Logical-ExpressionOracle function:

```
oracle = LogicalExpressionOracle(expression)
```

Where the expression is the logical expression explained earlier. Then pass the oracle in to the Grover function:

```
grover = Grover(oracle)
```

Step 4 : Run the algorithm

Next we just need to run the algorithm using grover.run():

```
result = grover.run(backend, shots=1024)
```

Where backend is the quantum device that the algorithm is run on and shots is the number of times we run the algorithm.

Step 5: Obtain the results

Next we need to get the results using the following code:

```
counts = result['measurement']
```

26.2 Code

```
from qiskit import IBMQ
from qiskit.aqua.algorithms import Grover
from qiskit.aqua.components.oracles import
    LogicalExpressionOracle

IBMQ.enable_account('ENTER API KEY HERE')
```

```
provider = IBMQ.get_provider(hub='ibm-q')

backend = provider.get_backend('ibmq_qasm_simulator')

expression = '(a & b)& ~(c)'

oracle = LogicalExpressionOracle(expression)
grover = Grover(oracle)

result = grover.run(backend, shots=1024)

counts = result['measurement']

print(counts)
print('Press any key to close')
input()
```

26.3 Output

```
{'000': 28, '001': 34, '010': 37, '011': 799, '100': 30, '101': 31, '110': 32, '111': 33}
Press any key to close
```

Figure 26.1: Output displaying the results for the expression (A AND B) OR (C). Notice how 011 has the most measurements as it satisfies the expression.

27 Qiskit: Evaluating Truth Tables with Grover's Search

In the last chapter we learned how to evaluate logical expressions using Grover's search. In this tutorial we will explore how to use Grover's search to instead evaluate truth tables.

A truth table can be defined as a table that shows the output of a function given each combination of a number of inputs.With a truth table we may want to see what inputs will make the output true. For a small number of inputs this can be fairly straight forward. However if a truth table has a large number of outputs it can become quite difficult to evaluate. However with Grover's Search we can evaluate the table in only $O(\sqrt{n})$ time.

27.1 Implementation

Grover's search for truth tables can be implemented very easily in Qiskit with the following steps:

27.1.1 Step 1: Find the bit string for the truth table

The first step is to specify the bit string associated with the truth table as this will be the input for our oracle. For any truth table the bit string is simply the function/output column. For example consider the following truth table:

A	B	F
0	0	0
0	1	0
1	0	0
1	1	1

Table 27.1:

Column F is our bit string ie '0001'

Another example:

A	B	F
0	0	1
0	1	1
1	0	1
1	1	0

Table 27.2:

Here the bit string would be '1110'

Rule of thumb is for a truth table consisting of N variables the bit string will be 2^n. For example if we have 4 variables in our truth table the bit string will have a length of 16.

27.1.2 Step 2: Pass the bit string in to the TruthTableOracle functon

The second step is to specify the correct oracle. Since we are evaluating truth tables you will need to pass the bit string in to the TruthTableOracle function:

```
expression = '11000001' # Our bit string
oracle = TruthTableOracle(expression)
```

Then pass the oracle in to the Grover function:

```
grover = Grover(oracle)
```

27.1.3 Step 4 : Run the algorithm

Next we just need to run the algorithm using grover.run():

```
result = grover.run(backend, shots=1024)
```

Where backend is the quantum device that the algorithm is run on and shots is the number of times we run the algorithm.

27.1.4 Step 5: Obtain the results

Next we need to get the results using the following code:

```
counts = result['measurement']
```

27.2 How to run the program

- Copy and paste the code below in to a python file
- Enter your API token in the IBMQ.enable_account('Insert API token here') part
- Save and run

27.3 Code

```
from qiskit import IBMQ
from qiskit.aqua.algorithms import Grover
from qiskit.aqua.components.oracles import TruthTableOracle

IBMQ.enable_account('ENTER API KEY HERE')
provider = IBMQ.get_provider(hub='ibm-q')

backend = provider.get_backend('ibmq_qasm_simulator')

expression = '11000001'

oracle = TruthTableOracle(expression)

print(oracle)

grover = Grover(oracle)

result = grover.run(backend, shots=1024)

counts = result['measurement']

print('\nTruth tables with Grovers Search')
print('------------------------------\n')
```

```
print('Bit string is ', expression)
print('\nResults ',counts)
print('\nPress any key to close')
input()
```

27.4 Output

Figure 27.1: From the results we can see that the correct inputs
are 000, 001, and 111

28 Satisfying k-SAT problems with Grover's Search

28.1 Introduction

The k-SAT problem is a Boolean satisfiable problem with k literals. Given a Boolean formula consisting of a number of clauses each with k literals the goal is to find what inputs will satisfy the problem. For example take the following formula:

$$F = (\overline{A} \vee B \vee C) \wedge (A \vee \overline{B} \vee C) \wedge (A \vee B \vee \overline{C}) \wedge (\overline{A} \vee B \vee \overline{C})$$
$$(28.1)$$

This is k-SAT problem consisting of 4 clauses and 3 literals in each clause. The clauses are the terms encased in brackets while the literals are the variables in each clause. The over-line above a variable denotes a negation of that variable. The symbol denotes the AND operation while denotes the OR operation. Because there is 3 literals in each clause this k-SAT problem is known as a 3-SAT problem.

As the number of variables and clauses increases in the expression the more harder it is for a classical computer to evaluate the expression. However using Grover's search algorithm we can find the variable combinations needed that will satisfy the boolean expression. Grover's algorithm has a huge advantage over classical methods as the time complexity is only

$O(\sqrt{n})$.

28.2 Implementation

In Qiskit solving a k-SAT problem with Grover's Search can be done with the following steps:

28.2.1 Step 1: Encode the k-sat problem in to DIMACS format

The first step is to express the k-SAT problem in to DIMACS CNF format. DIMACS CNF is a format used in Qiskit to define Boolean expressions. For example consider the following 4-SAT problem:

$$F = (\overline{A} \vee B \vee C \vee D) \wedge (A \vee \overline{B} \vee C \vee D) \wedge (A \vee B \vee \overline{C} \vee D) \wedge (A \vee B \vee C \vee \overline{D}) \wedge (A \vee B \vee \overline{C} \vee \overline{D})$$

(28.2)

In DIMACS CNF format this can be:

```
expression = '''
c 4-SAT
p cnf 4 5
-1 2 3 4 0
1 -2 3 4 0
1 2 -3 4 0
1 2 3 -4 0
1 2 -3 -4 0
'''
```

- c denotes a comment

- p denotes the start of the problem line

- cnf denotes the problem type (conjunctive normal form)

- 4 and 5 after cnf denote the number of variables and clauses

- 0 marks the end of each clause in the expression

28.2.2 Step 2: Specify the oracle and pass to the Grover function

The first step is to specify the correct oracle. Since we are evaluating a k-SAT problem you will need to use the LogicalExpressionOracle function:

```
oracle = LogicalExpressionOracle(expression)
```

Then pass the oracle in to the Grover function:

```
grover = Grover(oracle)
```

28.2.3 Step 3 : Run the algorithm

Next we just need to run the algorithm using grover.run():

```
result = grover.run(backend, shots=1024)
```

Where backend is the quantum device that the algorithm is run on and shots is the number of times we run the algorithm.

28.2.4 Step 4: Obtain the results

Next we need to get the results using the following code:

```
counts = result['measurement']
```

28.3 How to run the program

- Copy and paste the code below in to a python file

- Enter your API token in the IBMQ.enable_account('Insert API token here') part

- Save and run

28.4 Code

```
from qiskit import IBMQ
from qiskit.aqua.algorithms import Grover
from qiskit.aqua.components.oracles import
    LogicalExpressionOracle

IBMQ.enable_account('ENTER API KEY HERE')
provider = IBMQ.get_provider(hub='ibm-q')

backend = provider.get_backend('ibmq_qasm_simulator')

expression = '''
c 4-SAT
p cnf 4 5
-1 2 3 4 0
1 -2 3 4 0
```

```
1 2 -3 4 0
1 2 3 -4 0
1 2 -3 -4 0
'''
oracle = LogicalExpressionOracle(expression)
grover = Grover(oracle)

result = grover.run(backend, shots=1024)
counts = result['measurement']

print('\n4SAT with Grovers Search')
print('-----------------------------\n')
print('4SAT: ', expression)
print('\nResults ',counts)
print('\nPress any key to close')
input()
```

28.5 Output

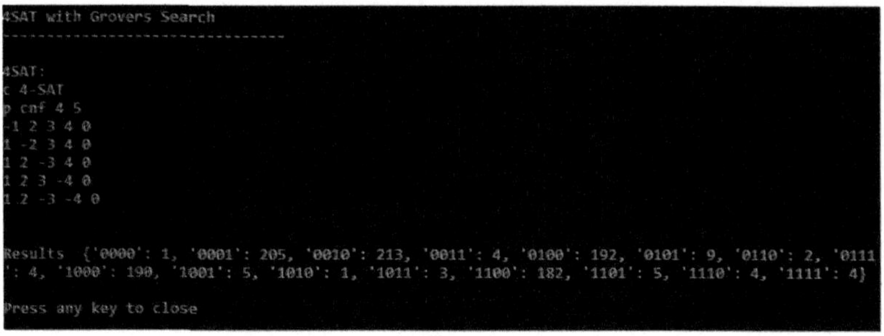

Figure 28.1: Output from the above code

29 Qiskit: Quantum Error Correction with Bit flip code

Qubits are very fragile and are prone to errors due to decoherence and other quantum noise. However using quantum error correction qubit errors can be corrected. In this tutorial you will see how a specific type of error called a bit flip error can be corrected using a quantum circuit known as the bit flip code.

29.1 What is a Bit Flip error?

A bit flip error is specific type of error where the qubits computational state flips from $|1\rangle$ to $|0\rangle$ or vice versa. However a bit flip can be corrected using the bit flip code. This is a 3 qubit circuit that makes use of 2 ancillary qubits to correct 1 qubit.

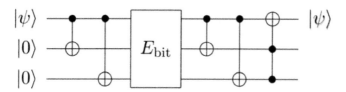

Figure 29.1: Circuit diagram of the bit flip code

The code works by first using CNOT gates to transfer the computational state of the main qubit to the other ancillary qubits. Then if an error occurs the first qubits state will be flipped. To correct the bit flip CNOT gates are applied to the ancillary qubits again and then a toffoli gate is applied to the first qubit which will correct its state. For example let's say the main qubits state was $|0\rangle$. CNOT gates will be applied to the ancillary qubits which will leave them unchanged since the main qubits state was $|0\rangle$. Next a bit flip occurs which flips the main qubits state to $|1\rangle$. After the bit flip CNOT gates are applied to the ancillary qubits which will flip their states to $|1\rangle$ since the main qubits state is $|1\rangle$. Then a toffoli gate is applied to the main qubit which will flip the state of the qubit since the ancillary qubits states are $|1\rangle$. This flips the state of the main qubit to $|0\rangle$ thus correcting the error.

29.2 Implementation

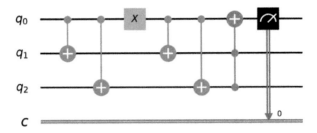

Figure 29.2: Circuit diagram of bit flip code with simulated error using a NOT gate

29.2.1 Step 1: Initialise the quantum and classical registers

The first step is to initialise a 3 qubit register . This is done by the following code:

```
q = QuantumRegister(3,'q')
```

Next we initialise the 1 bit classical register with the following code:

```
c = ClassicalRegister(1,'c')
```

29.2.2 Step 2: Create the circuit

Next we create quantum circuit using the following code:

```
circuit = QuantumCircuit(q,c)
```

29.2.3 Step 3: Apply a CNOT gate to ancillary qubits

Next we will need to transfer the state of the first qubit to the ancillary qubits. This is done using CNOT gates where the ancillary qubits are the targets and the first qubit is the control qubit.

This is done using the following code:

```
circuit.cx(q[0],q[1])
circuit.cx(q[0],q[2])
```

29.2.4 Step 4: Simulate a bit flip

To show that the circuit corrects bit flips lets simulate a bit flip error. This can be done by applying a NOT gate to the first qubit:

```
circuit.x(q[0]) #Add this to simulate a bit flip error
```

Step 5: Again apply CNOT gates to ancillary qubits

This is done using the following code:

```
circuit.cx(q[0],q[1])
circuit.cx(q[0],q[2])
```

29.2.5 Step 6: Apply a toffoli gate to to main qubit

This is done using the following code:

```
circuit.ccx(q[2],q[1],q[0])
```

29.2.6 Step 7: Measure the qubits

After this we measure the qubits.
  This is done with the following code:

```
circuit.measure(q,c)
```

29.3 How to run the program

- Copy and paste the code below in to a python file
- Enter your API token in the IBMQ.enable_account('Insert API token here') part
- Save and run

29.4 Code

```
from qiskit import QuantumRegister
from qiskit import QuantumRegister, ClassicalRegister
from qiskit import QuantumCircuit, execute,IBMQ
from qiskit.tools.monitor import job_monitor

print('\nBit Flip Code')
print('----------------')

IBMQ.enable_account('ENTER API KEY HERE')
provider = IBMQ.get_provider(hub='ibm-q')

backend = provider.get_backend('ibmq_qasm_simulator')

q = QuantumRegister(3,'q')
c = ClassicalRegister(1,'c')

circuit = QuantumCircuit(q,c)

circuit.cx(q[0],q[1])
circuit.cx(q[0],q[2])
circuit.x(q[0]) #Add this to simulate a bit flip error
circuit.cx(q[0],q[1])
circuit.cx(q[0],q[2])
```

```
circuit.ccx(q[2],q[1],q[0])
circuit.measure(q[0],c[0])

job = execute(circuit, backend, shots=1000)

job_monitor(job)

counts = job.result().get_counts()

print("\nBit flip code with error")
print("---------------------")
print(counts)
input()
```

30 Qiskit: Quantum Error Correction with Phase flip code

In our last tutorial we explored how to correct bit flip errors using the bit flip code. However bit flip errors are not the only potential errors. There is a type of error called a phase flip error. In this tutorial you will see how a specific type of qubit error called a phase flip can be corrected using a quantum circuit known as the phase flip code.

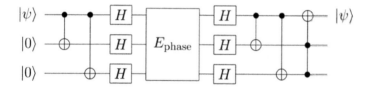

Figure 30.1: Circuit diagram of the phase flip code

30.1 What is a Phase flip error?

A phase flip error is a type of error that effects the phase of the qubit. In essence this error is equivalent to a Z-gate. However as said before it can be corrected using the phase flip code. The phase flip code works identically to the bit flip code in that it first transfers the state of the main qubit to the ancillary qubits using CNOT gates. Next all qubits are put in to superposition using a Hadamard gate.

After this a phase flip error will occur on the main qubit which will effect its phase. After this a Hadamard gate is applied to all qubits again which will take them out of superposition since two Hadamard gates applied leave the state of the qubits unchanged.

However because the main qubits phase was changed it will not be in it's previous state but flipped from 1 to 0 or vice versa. Because this has altered the computational state of the qubit we can correct this using CNOT gates and a Toffoli gate where the main qubit is the target and the control qubits are the ancillary qubits.

30.2 Implementation

30.2.1 Step 1: Intialise the quantum and classical registers

The first step is to initialise a 3 qubit register . This is done by the following code:

```
q = QuantumRegister(3,'q')
```

Next we initialise the 1 bit classical register with the following code:

```
c = ClassicalRegister(1,'c')
```

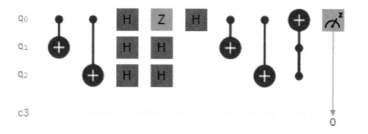

Figure 30.2: Circuit diagram of the phase flip code

30.2.2 Step 2: Create the circuit

Next we create quantum circuit using the following code:

```
circuit = QuantumCircuit(q,c)
```

30.2.3 Step 3: Apply a CNOT gate to ancillary qubits

Next we will need to transfer the state of the first qubit to the ancillary qubits. This is done using CNOT gates where the ancillary qubits are the targets and the first qubit is the control qubit.

This is done using the following code:

```
circuit.cx(q[0],q[1])
circuit.cx(q[0],q[2])
```

30.2.4 Step 4: Apply hadamard gates to all qubits

This puts the qubits in to superposition and is done using the following code:

```
circuit.h(q[0])
circuit.h(q[1])
circuit.h(q[2])
```

30.2.5 Step 5: Simulate a phase flip

To show that the circuit corrects phase flips lets simulate a bit flip error. This can be done by applying a z-gate to the first qubit:

```
circuit.z(q[0]) #Add this to simulate a bit flip error
```

30.2.6 Step 6: Bring all qubits out of superposition by applying hadamard gates again

This will bring the qubits out of superposition and is done using the following code:

```
circuit.h(q[0])
circuit.h(q[1])
circuit.h(q[2])
```

30.2.7 Step 7: Again apply CNOT gates to ancillary qubits

This is done using the following code:

```
circuit.cx(q[0],q[1])
circuit.cx(q[0],q[2])
```

30.2.8 Step 8: Apply a toffoli gate to to main qubit

This is done using the following code:

```
circuit.ccx(q[2],q[1],q[0])
```

30.2.9 Step 9: Measure the qubits

After this we measure the qubits.
This is done with the following code:

```
circuit.measure(q,c)
```

30.3 How to run the program

- Copy and paste the code below in to a python file

- Enter your API token in the IBMQ.enable_account('Insert API token here') part

- Save and run

30.4 Code

```
from qiskit import QuantumRegister
from qiskit import QuantumRegister, ClassicalRegister
from qiskit import QuantumCircuit, execute,IBMQ
from qiskit.tools.monitor import job_monitor

print('\nPhase Flip Code')
print('----------------')

IBMQ.enable_account('ENTER API KEY HERE')
provider = IBMQ.get_provider(hub='ibm-q')

backend = provider.get_backend('ibmq_qasm_simulator')

q = QuantumRegister(3,'q')
c = ClassicalRegister(1,'c')

circuit = QuantumCircuit(q,c)

circuit.cx(q[0],q[1])
circuit.cx(q[0],q[2])
circuit.h(q[0])
circuit.h(q[1])
circuit.h(q[2])
circuit.z(q[0]) #Add this to simulate a phase flip error
circuit.h(q[0])
circuit.h(q[1])
circuit.h(q[2])
circuit.cx(q[0],q[1])
circuit.cx(q[0],q[2])
circuit.ccx(q[2],q[1],q[0])
circuit.measure(q[0],c[0])
```

```
job = execute(circuit, backend, shots=1000)

job_monitor(job)

counts = job.result().get_counts()

print("\nPhase flip code with error")
print("---------------------")
print(counts)
input()
```

30.5 Output

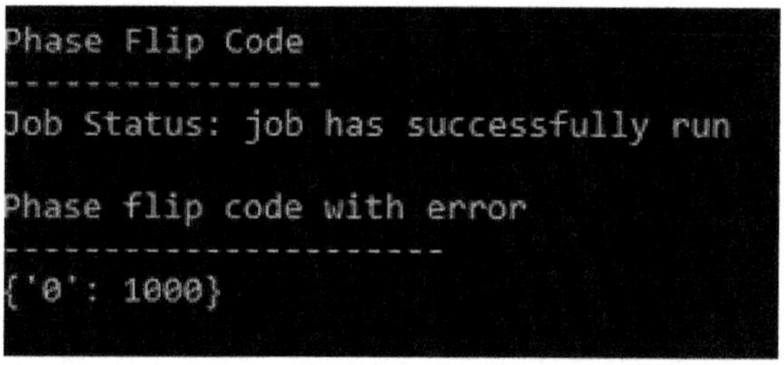

Figure 30.3: Output showing the main qubit has been corrected to 0

31 Qiskit: Quantum Error Correction with the Shor code

In the last chapters we explored how to correct bit flips and phase flips. While the bit flip code can correct bit flips and the phase flip code can correct phase flips they cannot correct both types of error. However there is a quantum circuit called the Shor code that can correct both bit flip errors as well as phase flip errors.

The Shor code is a 9 qubit circuit that requires 8 ancillary qubits to correct 1 qubit. For simplification we will call the 1st qubit that we want to correct the main qubit and the ancillary qubits 1 to 8. If you have seen our tutorials on the bit flip and phase flip circuit then the Shor code will look very familiar as it uses the same gates and ordering.

The Shor code works by first taking the computational state of the main qubit and transferring it to the 3rd and 6th qubit. These qubits are used for correcting phase errors. After this these qubits are put in to superposition using a Hadamard gate. Next the states of the main qubit as well as the 3rd, and 6th qubits use CNOT gates to transfer their states to ancillary qubits responsible for correcting bit flips. More specifically the main qubit transfers its state to the 1st and 2nd ancillary qubit. The 3rd transfers it state to the 4th and 5th. The 6th transfer its state to the 7th and 8th qubit.

After this a bit flip or phase flip may occur on the main qubit. in the diagram above this is denoted as E. Next the previous step is repeated. Toffoli gates are then applied to the main qubit as well as the 3rd and 6th qubit where the control qubits are the auxiliary qubits responsible for phase correction.

After this Hadamard gates are applied to the main qubit as well as the 3rd and 6th qubit to bring them out of superposition. Then CNOT gates are applied to the 3rd and 6th qubit where the control qubit is the main qubit. Finally a toffoli gate is applied to the main qubit which is controlled by the 3rd and 6th qubit.

31.1 Implementation

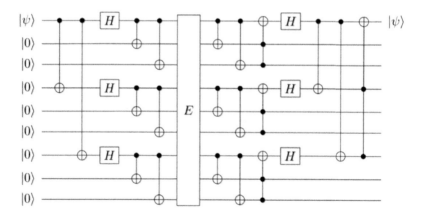

In order to simulate a bit flip and phase error a Pauli-X gate and a Pauli-Z gate will be applied to the main qubit as seen in the circuit diagram above. The Pauli-X gate will simulate a bit flip while the Z gate will simulate a phase flip.

In the code below these simulated errors are implemented using the following:

```
circuit.x(q[0])#Bit flip error
circuit.z(q[0])#Phase flip error
```

31.2 How to run the program

- Copy and paste the code below in to a python file

- Enter your API token in the IBMQ.enable_account('Insert API token here') part

- Save and run

31.3 Code

```
print('\nShor Code')
print('--------------')

from qiskit import QuantumRegister
from qiskit import ClassicalRegister
from qiskit import QuantumCircuit, execute,IBMQ
from qiskit.tools.monitor import job_monitor

IBMQ.enable_account(ENTER API KEY HERE')
provider = IBMQ.get_provider(hub='ibm-q')
```

```
backend = provider.get_backend('ibmq_qasm_simulator')

q = QuantumRegister(1,'q')
c = ClassicalRegister(1,'c')

circuit = QuantumCircuit(q,c)

circuit.h(q[0])

####error here############
circuit.x(q[0])#Bit flip error
circuit.z(q[0])#Phase flip error
############################

circuit.h(q[0])

circuit.barrier(q)

circuit.measure(q[0],c[0])

job = execute(circuit, backend, shots=1000)

job_monitor(job)

counts = job.result().get_counts()

print("\n Uncorrected bit flip and phase error")
print("-----------------------------------")
print(counts)

#####Shor code starts here ########
q = QuantumRegister(9,'q')
c = ClassicalRegister(1,'c')

circuit = QuantumCircuit(q,c)
```

211

```
circuit.cx(q[0],q[3])
circuit.cx(q[0],q[6])

circuit.h(q[0])
circuit.h(q[3])
circuit.h(q[6])

circuit.cx(q[0],q[1])
circuit.cx(q[3],q[4])
circuit.cx(q[6],q[7])

circuit.cx(q[0],q[2])
circuit.cx(q[3],q[5])
circuit.cx(q[6],q[8])

circuit.barrier(q)

####error here###########
circuit.x(q[0])#Bit flip error
circuit.z(q[0])#Phase flip error
###########################

circuit.barrier(q)
circuit.cx(q[0],q[1])
circuit.cx(q[3],q[4])
circuit.cx(q[6],q[7])

circuit.cx(q[0],q[2])
circuit.cx(q[3],q[5])
circuit.cx(q[6],q[8])

circuit.ccx(q[1],q[2],q[0])
circuit.ccx(q[4],q[5],q[3])
circuit.ccx(q[8],q[7],q[6])
```

```
circuit.h(q[0])
circuit.h(q[3])
circuit.h(q[6])

circuit.cx(q[0],q[3])
circuit.cx(q[0],q[6])
circuit.ccx(q[6],q[3],q[0])

circuit.barrier(q)

circuit.measure(q[0],c[0])

circuit.draw(output='mpl',filename='shorcode.png') #Draws
    an image of the circuit

job = execute(circuit, backend, shots=1000)

job_monitor(job)

counts = job.result().get_counts()

print("\nShor code with bit flip and phase error")
print("--------------------------------------")
print(counts)
input()
```

31.4 Output

```
Uncorrected bit flip and phase error
------------------------------------
{'1': 1000}

Job Status: job has successfully run

Shor code with bit flip and phase error
----------------------------------------
{'0': 1000}
```

Figure 31.1: Output of the code. First part shows how a bit flip
and phase flip have flipped the value to 1. Second
part shows the Shor code has corrected the qubit
flip to 0.

32 Qiskit: Quantum Fourier Transform

32.1 What is a Quantum Fourier Transform?

The Quantum Fourier Transform (QFT) is a circuit that transforms the state of the qubit from the computational basis to the Fourier basis. Note that the Fourier basis is just another term for the Hadamard basis. As such the easiest way to implement a QFT is with Hadamard gates and Controlled U1 gates.

Note: A Controlled U1 gate is just a gate that implements a single rotation around the Z-axis (phase) of the target qubit if the control qubit is $|1\rangle$.

32.2 1 Qubit QFT

The simplest QFT is a 1 qubit QFT which just implements a Hadamard gate.

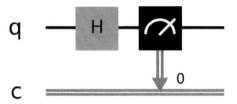

Figure 32.1: Circuit diagram of a 1 qubit QFT circuit

32.3 2 Qubit QFT

However if we implement a 2 qubit QFT then you can see how the controlled U1 are used:

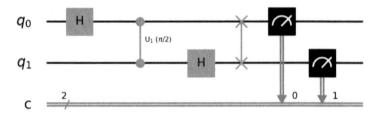

Figure 32.2: Circuit diagram of a 2 qubit QFT circuit

First we implement a hadamard gate which puts q_0 in to superposition. Next we apply a controlled U1 gate with a rotation of $\frac{\pi}{2}$ to q_1. After this a hadamard gate is applied to q_1. Next we apply a swap gate to q_0 and q_1. Note that these swap gates are not needed if the QFT is implemented at the end of your circuit.

After this both qubits will be in superposition but whatever computational value ($|1\rangle$ or $|0\rangle$) will be encoded in to the hadamard basis of the qubit To encode values on N qubits we have to double the rotation value of each qubit. For example the diagram below shows a 5 qubit QFT. Notice how for q_0 it applies a rotation of $\frac{\pi}{2}$ for q_1 then $\frac{\pi}{4}$ for q_2 then $\frac{\pi}{8}$ for q_3 and so on. This pattern repeats for each qubit. When all rotations have been applied to a qubit it is put in to superposition using a hadamard gate. Then it can be used as a control qubit to apply rotations to target qubits below it.

32.4 Implementation

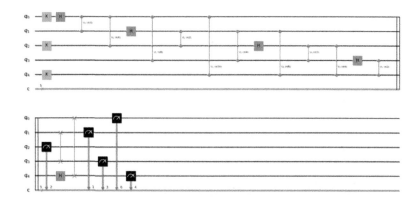

Figure 32.3: Circuit diagram of a 5 qubit QFT circuit

32.4.1 Implementing a 5 qubit quantum fourier transform in qiskit

In qiskit we could implement the 5 qubit QFT by implementing all the gates in the diagram above. Thankfully qiskit has a QFT function that we can use to make everything simpler!

In qiskit you can use the QFT function as follows:

```
QFT(num_qubits=None, approximation_degree=0,
    do_swaps=True, inverse=False, insert_barriers=False,
    name='qft')
```

Where:

- num_qubits: The number of qubits we want to add to the QFT (in our case it is 5)

- approximation_degree: This allows us to reduce circuit depth by ignoring phase rotations under a certain value

- do_swaps: If set to true then we use swap gates in the QFT

- inverse: If set to true we implement the inverse QFT

- insert barrier: If set to true then we insert barriers

For example in our 5 qubit QFT we implement the following:

```
QFT(num_qubits=5, approximation_degree=0, do_swaps=True,
    inverse=False, insert_barriers=True, name='qft')
```

If we encode 1010 on to a QFT and then measure it we will get random values since the qubits have been put in to superposition and the values we encoded in to the computational basis are now encoded in the hadamard basis of each qubit via the controlled U1 gates.

32.4.2 Inverse Quantum Fourier Transform

To get our values back we can use the inverse QFT. This reverses all the rotations done in the QFT above. For example is there was a rotation of Pi in the QFT then the inverse QFT will do a rotation of $-\pi$. In Qiskit we can get the values back by implementing an inverse QFT by setting inverse to true.

For example:

```
QFT(num_qubits=5, approximation_degree=0, do_swaps=True,
    inverse=True, insert_barriers=True, name='qft')
```

32.5 How to run the program

- Copy and paste the code below in to a python file

- Enter your API token in the IBMQ.enable_account('Insert API token here') part

- Save and run

32.6 Code

```
from qiskit import QuantumRegister, ClassicalRegister
from qiskit import QuantumCircuit, execute,IBMQ
from qiskit.tools.monitor import job_monitor
from qiskit.circuit.library import QFT
import numpy as np

pi = np.pi

IBMQ.enable_account(ENTER API KEY  HERE )
provider = IBMQ.get_provider(hub='ibm-q')

backend = provider.get_backend('ibmq_qasm_simulator')

q = QuantumRegister(5,'q')
c = ClassicalRegister(5,'c')
```

```
circuit = QuantumCircuit(q,c)

circuit.x(q[4])
circuit.x(q[2])
circuit.x(q[0])
circuit += QFT(num_qubits=5, approximation_degree=0,
    do_swaps=True, inverse=False, insert_barriers=False,
    name='qft')
circuit.measure(q,c)
circuit.draw(output='mpl', filename='qft1.png')
print(circuit)

job = execute(circuit, backend, shots=1000)

job_monitor(job)

counts = job.result().get_counts()

print("\n QFT Output")
print("-------------")
print(counts)
input()

q = QuantumRegister(5,'q')
c = ClassicalRegister(5,'c')

circuit = QuantumCircuit(q,c)

circuit.x(q[4])
circuit.x(q[2])
circuit.x(q[0])
circuit += QFT(num_qubits=5, approximation_degree=0,
    do_swaps=True, inverse=False, insert_barriers=True,
    name='qft')
```

```
circuit += QFT(num_qubits=5, approximation_degree=0,
    do_swaps=True, inverse=True, insert_barriers=True,
    name='qft')
circuit.measure(q,c)
circuit.draw(output='mpl',filename='qft2.png')

print(circuit)

job = execute(circuit, backend, shots=1000)

job_monitor(job)

counts = job.result().get_counts()

print("\n QFT with inverse QFT Output")
print("----------------------------")
print(counts)
input()
```

32.7 Output

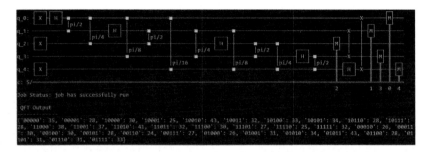

Figure 32.4: Output when running the 5 qubit QFT. Notice how we get multiple values back since the qubits are in superposition and the value is encoded in the Hadamard basis.

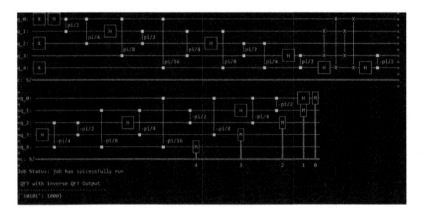

Figure 32.5: Here the output when running the QFT with the inverse QFT. Notice how we get the 1010 back!

33 Qiskit: Quantum error correction with the Shor code

33.1 Introduction

In our last quantum error correction tutorials we looked at how to correct phase errors and bit flip errors. Each of these errors has a circuit that can be used to correct that particular error but not the other type. For example the bit flip code cannot correct phase errors and phase flip code cannot correct bit flip errors.

However there is a specific error correction circuit known as the Shor code which can correct both phase flips as well as bit flip errors. In this tutorial we will explore what the Shor code is and how to implement it in Qiskit.

33.1.1 What is the Shor Code?

The Shor code is a 9 qubit circuit that requires 8 ancillary qubits to correct 1 qubit. For simplification we will call the 1st qubit that we want to correct the main qubit and the ancillary qubits 1 to 8. If you have seen our tutorials on the bit flip and phase flip circuit then the Shor code will look very familiar as it uses the same gates and ordering.

The Shor code works by first taking the computational state of the main qubit and transferring it to the 3rd and 6th qubit. These qubits are used for correcting phase errors. After this

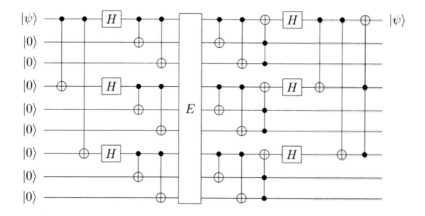

Figure 33.1: Circuit Diagram of the Shor Code

these qubits are put in to superposition using a Hadamard gate. Next the states of the main qubit as well as the 3rd, and 6th qubits use CNOT gates to transfer their states to ancillary qubits responsible for correcting bit flips. More specifically the main qubit transfers its state to the 1st and 2nd ancillary qubit. The 3rd transfers it state to the 4th and 5th. The 6th transfer its state to the 7th and 8th qubit.

After this a bit flip or phase flip may occur on the main qubit. in the diagram above this is denoted as E. Next the previous step is repeated. Toffoli gates are then applied to the main qubit as well as the 3rd and 6th qubit where the control qubits are the auxiliary qubits responsible for phase correction.

After this Hadamard gates are applied to the main qubit as well as the 3rd and 6th qubit to bring them out of superposition.

Then CNOT gates are applied to the 3rd and 6th qubit where the control qubit is the main qubit. Finally a toffoli gate is applied to the main qubit which is controlled by the 3rd and 6th qubit.

33.2 Implementation

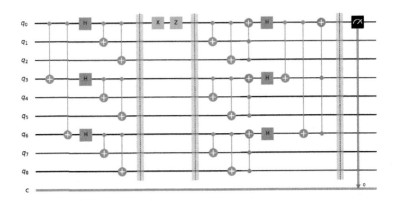

Figure 33.2: Circuit diagram of Shor code with bit flip and phase flip error

In order to simulate a bit flip and phase error a Pauli-X gate and a Pauli-Z gate will be applied to the main qubit as seen in the circuit diagram above. The Pauli-X gate will simulate a bit flip while the Z gate will simulate a phase flip.

In the code below these simulated errors are implemented using the following:

226

```
circuit.x(q[0])#Bit flip error
circuit.z(q[0])#Phase flip error
```

33.3 How to run the program

- Copy and paste the code below in to a python file

- Enter your API token in the IBMQ.enable_account('Insert API token here') part

- Save and run

33.4 Code

```
print('\nShor Code')
print('--------------')

from qiskit import QuantumRegister
from qiskit import ClassicalRegister
from qiskit import QuantumCircuit, execute,IBMQ
from qiskit.tools.monitor import job_monitor

IBMQ.enable_account(ENTER API KEY HERE')
provider = IBMQ.get_provider(hub='ibm-q')

backend = provider.get_backend('ibmq_qasm_simulator')

q = QuantumRegister(1,'q')
c = ClassicalRegister(1,'c')

circuit = QuantumCircuit(q,c)
```

```
circuit.h(q[0])

####error here############
circuit.x(q[0])#Bit flip error
circuit.z(q[0])#Phase flip error
###########################

circuit.h(q[0])

circuit.barrier(q)

circuit.measure(q[0],c[0])

job = execute(circuit, backend, shots=1000)

job_monitor(job)

counts = job.result().get_counts()

print("\n Uncorrected bit flip and phase error")
print("-----------------------------------")
print(counts)

#####Shor code starts here ########
q = QuantumRegister(9,'q')
c = ClassicalRegister(1,'c')

circuit = QuantumCircuit(q,c)

circuit.cx(q[0],q[3])
circuit.cx(q[0],q[6])

circuit.h(q[0])
circuit.h(q[3])
```

```
circuit.h(q[6])

circuit.cx(q[0],q[1])
circuit.cx(q[3],q[4])
circuit.cx(q[6],q[7])

circuit.cx(q[0],q[2])
circuit.cx(q[3],q[5])
circuit.cx(q[6],q[8])

circuit.barrier(q)

####error here############
circuit.x(q[0])#Bit flip error
circuit.z(q[0])#Phase flip error
##########################

circuit.barrier(q)
circuit.cx(q[0],q[1])
circuit.cx(q[3],q[4])
circuit.cx(q[6],q[7])

circuit.cx(q[0],q[2])
circuit.cx(q[3],q[5])
circuit.cx(q[6],q[8])

circuit.ccx(q[1],q[2],q[0])
circuit.ccx(q[4],q[5],q[3])
circuit.ccx(q[8],q[7],q[6])

circuit.h(q[0])
circuit.h(q[3])
circuit.h(q[6])

circuit.cx(q[0],q[3])
```

```
circuit.cx(q[0],q[6])
circuit.ccx(q[6],q[3],q[0])

circuit.barrier(q)

circuit.measure(q[0],c[0])

circuit.draw(output='mpl',filename='shorcode.png') #Draws
    an image of the circuit

job = execute(circuit, backend, shots=1000)

job_monitor(job)

counts = job.result().get_counts()

print("\nShor code with bit flip and phase error")
print("-------------------------------------")
print(counts)
input()
```

33.5 Output

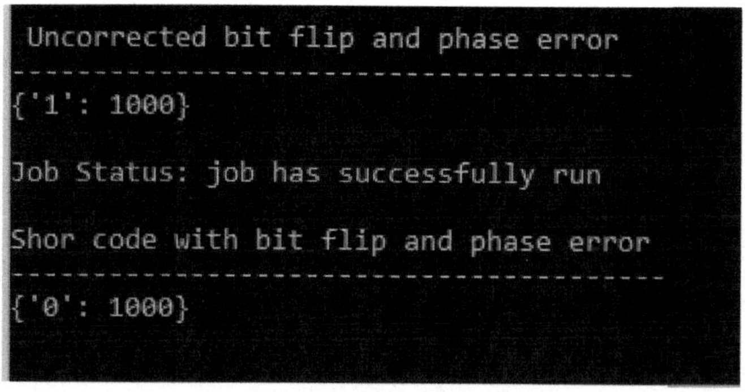

```
Uncorrected bit flip and phase error
-----------------------------------------
{'1': 1000}

Job Status: job has successfully run

Shor code with bit flip and phase error
-----------------------------------------
{'0': 1000}
```

Figure 33.3: Output of the code. First part shows how a bit flip and phase flip have flipped the value to 1. Second part shows the Shor code has corrected the qubit flip to 0.

34 Qiskit: Quantum Phase Estimation

Quantum Phase Estimation is a quantum algorithm that estimates the phase of a unitary operator. Phase estimation plays a very important role in a number of quantum algorithms such as Shor's algorithm.

34.1 How does it work

Quantum Phase estimation is essentially a quantum circuit consisting of two sets of qubits. The first set consists of counting qubits that are used to control unitary operations and the second set whom the unitary operations are applied to.

The steps in Phase Estimation are as follows:

34.1.1 Step 1: Put the counting qubits in to Superposition

The counting qubits are put in to superposition using hadamard gates.

34.1.2 Step 2: Apply unitary opertions to the second set

The main part of the circuit is to apply unitary operations on the second set. These unitary operations are essentially just controlled phase rotations of a specific angle. This angle is the phase that we wish to estimate. The first counting qubit will do 1 rotation while the second will do 2 rotations and the third will do 4 rotations and so on. For example lets say we have 4 qubits q_0 to q_3. The first 3 are the counting qubits and the 4th qubit is the qubit we wish to apply phase rotations to. The phase we wish to encode is pi/2. The first 3 qubits are put in to superposition. Next q_0 will control 1 phase rotation on q_3. Then q_1 will do 2 phase rotations on q_3 and q_2 will do 4 phase rotations on q_3. Note that each rotation will rotate q_3's phase by pi/2.

34.1.3 Step 3: Apply an inverse QFT

After these rotations an inverse QFT is applied to the counting qubits and they are measured.

A QFT or Quantum Fourier Transform is a circuit that transforms the state of the qubit from the computational basis to the Fourier basis. However in phase estimation we use the inverse QFT which puts the state in the Fourier basis in to the computational basis so we can measure it.

34.1.4 Step 4: Measure the counting qubits

After we have applied the inverse QFT we measure the qubits. If we have encoded a phase of pi/2 in to q_3 then we should get the binary value '010' which is 2.

To estimate the phase we use the following formula:

$$\theta = \frac{M}{2^n} \qquad (34.1)$$

Where θ is the estimated phase, M is the measured value, and n is the number of counting qubits. As such from the measurement above:

Which is correct since $\pi/2$ corresponds to a quarter rotation or 0.25.

34.2 Implementation

Next we will see how to implement quantum phase estimation in Qiskit so we can run it on real quantum devices!

For the implementation our circuit will consist of 4 qubits. The first 3 will be the counting qubits and the 4th will be qubit that we encode the unitary operations on.

For this example we will encode a phase of $2(\pi/3)$. This will correspond to a phase rotation of 1/3.

34.2.1 Step 1: Initialise the Quantum and Classical registers

This is done using the following code:

```
q = QuantumRegister(4,'q')
c = ClassicalRegister(3,'c')

circuit = QuantumCircuit(q,c)
```

Note that the quantum register consists of 4 qubits but the classical register consists of only 3 bits. This is because we only want to measure the 3 counting qubits whose values will be mapped to the classical register.

34.2.2 Step 2: Put the counting qubits in to Superposition

This is done by applying Hadamard gates with the following code:

```
circuit.h(q[0])
circuit.h(q[1])
circuit.h(q[2])
circuit.x(q[3]) # Flips Q[3] to 1
```

34.2.3 Step 3: Apply unitary operations

Now we can apply unitary operations with the specified phase angle (2*pi/3):

```
angle = 2*pi/3 #The phase angle we wish to encode

actual_phase = angle/(2*pi) # This is the actual phase
    rotation ie 0.5 would be half a rotation. Our expected
```

rotation will be 0.33.

```
circuit.cu1(angle, q[0], q[3]);#where angle is the
    rotation amount, q[0] is the control qubit and q[3] is
    the target qubit

circuit.cu1(angle, q[1], q[3]);
circuit.cu1(angle, q[1], q[3]);

circuit.cu1(angle, q[2], q[3]);
circuit.cu1(angle, q[2], q[3]);
circuit.cu1(angle, q[2], q[3]);
circuit.cu1(angle, q[2], q[3]);

circuit.barrier()
```

Note: cu1 is a rotational gate in qiskit which only rotates the phase of the qubit.

34.2.4 Step 4: Apply an inverse QFT

```
circuit.swap(q[0],q[2])
circuit.h(q[0])
circuit.cu1(-pi/2, q[0], q[1]);
circuit.h(q[1])
circuit.cu1(-pi/4, q[0], q[2]);
circuit.cu1(-pi/2, q[1], q[2]);
circuit.h(q[2])

circuit.barrier()
```

34.2.5 Step 5: Measure the qubits

```
#### Measuring counting qubits ####
circuit.measure(q[0],0)
circuit.measure(q[1],1)
circuit.measure(q[2],2)
```

34.2.6 Step 6: Run the circuit and obtain the results

Next we run the circuit by executing the job. Then we use the job monitor to monitor its progress and finally we obtain the counts.

```
job = execute(circuit, backend, shots=8192)
job_monitor(job)
counts = job.result().get_counts()
```

34.2.7 Step 7: Estimate the phase

When we obtain the counts we can use them to estimate the phase with the formula showing earlier.

```
print("Phase estimation output")
print("----------------------\n")

a = counts.most_frequent()

print('Most frequent measurement: ',a,'\n')

bin_a = int(a,2) # Converts the binary value to an integer
```

```
phase = bin_a/(2**3) # The calculation used to estimate
    the phase

print('Actual phase is: ',actual_phase)
print('Estimated phase is: ',phase)
input()
```

34.3 How to run the program

- Copy and paste the code below in to a python file

- Enter your API token in the IBMQ.enable_account('Insert API token here') part

- Save and run

34.4 Code

```
from qiskit import QuantumRegister, ClassicalRegister
from qiskit import QuantumCircuit, execute,IBMQ
from qiskit.tools.monitor import job_monitor
from qiskit.circuit.library import QFT
import numpy as np

IBMQ.enable_account('ENTER API KEY HERE')
provider = IBMQ.get_provider(hub='ibm-q')

backend = provider.get_backend('ibmq_qasm_simulator')

q = QuantumRegister(4,'q')
c = ClassicalRegister(3,'c')
```

```
circuit = QuantumCircuit(q,c)

pi = np.pi

angle = 2*(pi/3)

actual_phase = angle/(2*pi)


#### Controlled unitary operations ####
circuit.h(q[0])
circuit.h(q[1])
circuit.h(q[2])
circuit.x(q[3])

circuit.cu1(angle, q[0], q[3]);

circuit.cu1(angle, q[1], q[3]);
circuit.cu1(angle, q[1], q[3]);

circuit.cu1(angle, q[2], q[3]);
circuit.cu1(angle, q[2], q[3]);
circuit.cu1(angle, q[2], q[3]);
circuit.cu1(angle, q[2], q[3]);

circuit.barrier()

#### Inverse QFT ####
circuit.swap(q[0],q[2])
circuit.h(q[0])
circuit.cu1(-pi/2, q[0], q[1]);
circuit.h(q[1])
circuit.cu1(-pi/4, q[0], q[2]);
circuit.cu1(-pi/2, q[1], q[2]);
```

```
circuit.h(q[2])

circuit.barrier()

#### Measuring counting qubits ####
circuit.measure(q[0],0)
circuit.measure(q[1],1)
circuit.measure(q[2],2)

print(circuit)

job = execute(circuit, backend, shots=8192)

job_monitor(job)

counts = job.result().get_counts()

print('\n')
print("Phase estimation output")
print("----------------------\n")

a = counts.most_frequent()

print('Most frequent measurement: ',a,'\n')

bin_a = int(a,2) # Converts the binary value to an integer
phase = bin_a/(2**3)# The calculation used to estimate the
    phase


print('Actual phase is: ',actual_phase)
print('Estimated phase is: ',phase)
input()
```

34.5 Output

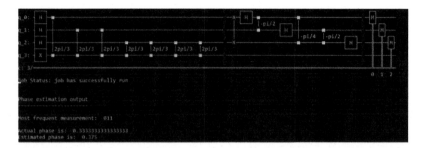

Figure 34.1: Output of the code showing the circuit and the actual and estimated phase

35 Qiskit: Modelling Probability Distributions

In this chapter we will explore how to model different probability distributions on IBMs quantum devices in Qiskit.

35.1 What are Probability Distributions?

Probability distributions are functions that give the probability of a given variable. In this tutorial we will look at 3 probability distributions:

- Normal Distribution

- Log-Normal Distribution

- Uniform Distribution

35.2 Normal Distribution

The normal distribution is a distribution that gives the probability of real random variables that are normally distributed. It also called the bell curve given its shape when plotted on a graph.

It can be defined as:

$$f(x) = \frac{1}{\sigma\sqrt{2\pi}}e^{-\frac{1}{2}(\frac{x-\mu}{\sigma})^2} \qquad (35.1)$$

Where μ is the mean and σ is the standard deviation.

When plotted the normal distribution looks like this:

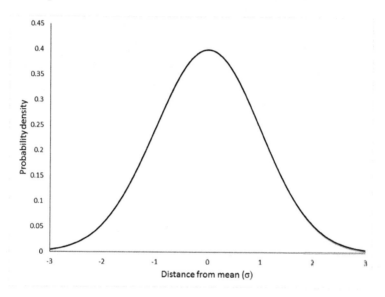

243

35.3 Uniform Distribution

The uniform distribution is a function where all random variables are equally probable within a certain range.

It can be defined using the following formula:

$$f(x) = \begin{cases} \frac{1}{b-a} & \text{for } a \le x \le b, \\ 0 & \text{for } x < a \text{ or } x > b, \end{cases} \qquad (35.2)$$

Where **b** and **a** are the upper and lower bounds respectively. When plotted the distribution looks like this:

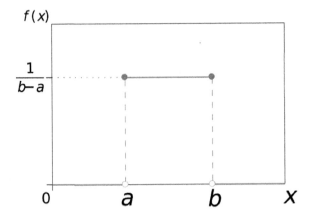

35.4 Log-Normal Distribution

The Log-Normal Distribution is much similar to the normal distribution except that the logarithm of the random variable is normally distributed.

It can be defined as:

$$f(x) = \frac{1}{x\sigma\sqrt{2\pi}} \exp\left(-\frac{(\ln x - \mu)^2}{2\sigma^2}\right) \qquad (35.3)$$

Where μ is the mean and σ is the standard deviation.

When plotted the distribution looks like this:

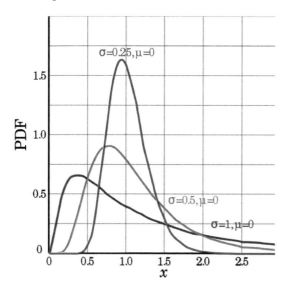

35.5 Implementation

In order to model the probability distributions we can use the following code:

35.5.1 Normal Distribution

The Normal Distribution can be modelled using the Normal Distribution function:

```
normal = NormalDistribution(num_target_qubits = 5, mu=0,
    sigma=1, low=- 1, high=1)
```

Where the number of qubits is set to 5 and mu = 0 and sigma = 1. After this the circuit has to be built using the following code:

```
normal.build(circuit,q)
```

The generated circuit used to model the normal distribution looks like this:

35.5.2 Uniform Distribution

The Uniform Distribution can be modelled using the UniformDistribution function:

```
uniform = UniformDistribution(num_target_qubits = 5,low=-
    0, high=1)
```

Where the number if target qubits is 5 and the lower bound is 0 and the upper bound is 1. Next the circuit has to be built and the qubits measured:

```
uniform.build(circuit,q)
```

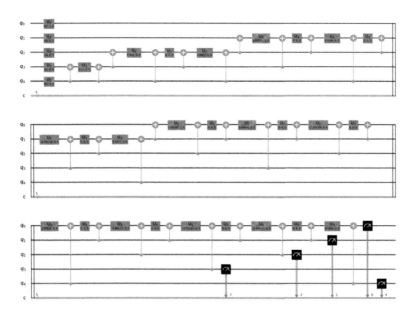

Figure 35.1: Circuit diagram for Normal distribution circuit

```
circuit.measure(q,c)
```

The generated circuit looks like the following:

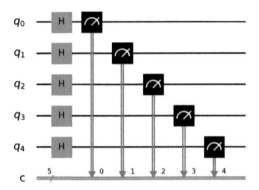

Figure 35.2: Circuit diagram for Uniform distribution circuit

This looks very much like a quantum random number generator because it is. Quantum devices ideally will be able to output random values that are uniformly distributed. However with noisy quantum devices the outcomes will not be perfectly uniformly distributed.

35.5.3 Log-Normal Distribution

The log-normal distribution can be modelled using the following function:

```
lognorm = LogNormalDistribution(num_target_qubits = 5,
    mu=0, sigma=1, low= 0, high=1)
```

Where the number of qubits is 5, mu is 0, and sigma is 1.

The lower bound is 0 and the upper bound is 1. After this the circuit is built and the qubits are measured:

```
lognorm.build(circuit,q)
circuit.measure(q,c)
```

The generated circuit looks like the following:

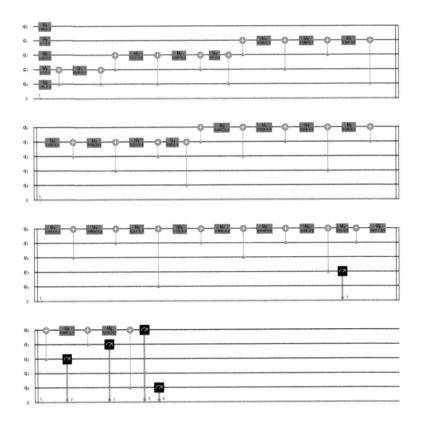

Figure 35.3: Circuit diagram for Log-Normal distribution circuit

35.6 How to run the program

- Copy and paste the code below in to a python file

- Enter your API token in the IBMQ.enable_account('Insert API token here') part

- Save and run

35.7 Code

```
from qiskit import QuantumRegister, ClassicalRegister,
    BasicAer
import numpy as np
import matplotlib.pyplot as plt
from qiskit import QuantumCircuit, execute,IBMQ
from qiskit.tools.monitor import job_monitor
from qiskit.aqua.components.uncertainty_models import
    NormalDistribution,UniformDistribution,LogNormalDistribution

IBMQ.enable_account('Enter API key')
provider = IBMQ.get_provider(hub='ibm-q')

backend = provider.get_backend('ibmq_qasm_simulator')

q = QuantumRegister(5,'q')
c = ClassicalRegister(5,'c')

print("\n Normal Distribution")
print("----------------")

circuit = QuantumCircuit(q,c)
normal = NormalDistribution(num_target_qubits = 5, mu=0,
    sigma=1, low=- 1, high=1)
```

```
normal.build(circuit,q)
circuit.measure(q,c)

job = execute(circuit, backend, shots=8192)
job_monitor(job)
counts = job.result().get_counts()

print(counts)
sortedcounts = []
sortedkeys = sorted(counts)

for i in sortedkeys:
    for j in counts:
        if(i == j):
            sortedcounts.append(counts.get(j))

plt.suptitle('Normal Distribution')
plt.plot(sortedcounts)
plt.show()

print("\n Uniform Distribution")
print("-----------------")

circuit = QuantumCircuit(q,c)
uniform = UniformDistribution(num_target_qubits = 5,low=-
    0, high=1)
uniform.build(circuit,q)
circuit.measure(q,c)

job = execute(circuit, backend, shots=8192)
job_monitor(job)
counts = job.result().get_counts()

print(counts)
```

```
sortedcounts = []
sortedkeys = sorted(counts)

for i in sortedkeys:
    for j in counts:
        if(i == j):
            sortedcounts.append(counts.get(j))

plt.suptitle('Uniform Distribution')
plt.plot(sortedcounts)
plt.show()

print("\n Log-Normal Distribution")
print("-----------------")

circuit = QuantumCircuit(q,c)
lognorm = LogNormalDistribution(num_target_qubits = 5,
    mu=0, sigma=1, low= 0, high=1)
lognorm.build(circuit,q)
circuit.measure(q,c)

job = execute(circuit, backend, shots=8192)
job_monitor(job)
counts = job.result().get_counts()

print(counts)

sortedcounts = []
sortedkeys = sorted(counts)

for i in sortedkeys:
    for j in counts:
        if(i == j):
            sortedcounts.append(counts.get(j))
```

```
plt.suptitle('Log-Normal Distribution')
plt.plot(sortedcounts)
plt.show()

input()
```

35.8 Output

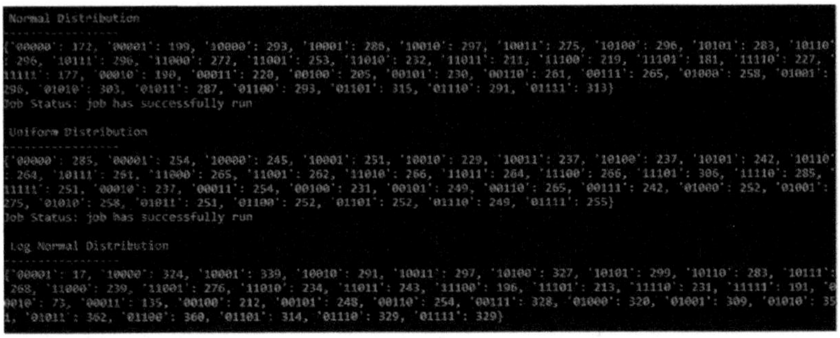

Figure 35.4: Output showing the probability distributions

35.8.1 Normal Distribution Plot

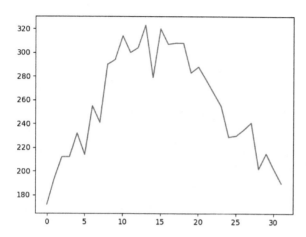

Figure 35.5: Graph plotted from the normal distribution variables

35.8.2 Uniform Distribution Plot

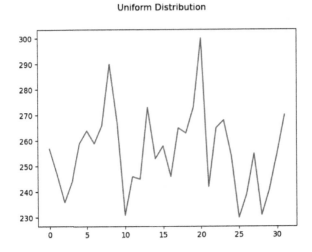

Figure 35.6: Graph plotted from the uniform distribution variables

35.8.3 Log-Normal Distribution Plot

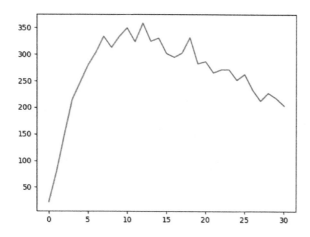

Figure 35.7: Graph plotted from the Log-Normal distribution variables

36 Qiskit: Creating Qubit Permutations

In this chapter we will explore how to create qubit permutations on IBM's quantum devices using the Permutation function in Qiskit.

36.1 What is a qubit permutation?

A qubit permutation is where qubit states are transferred to another qubit with the use of SWAP gates. For example consider 3 qubits. A permutation could be created where qubit 0 is mapped to qubit 1, qubit 1 is mapped to qubit 2 and qubit 2 is mapped to qubit 0.

36.2 Implementation

In Qiskit qubit permutations can by added using the permutation function:

```
Permutation(num_qubits, pattern=None, seed=None)
```

Where:

- *num_qubits* : is the number of qubits you want to permute

- *pattern* : is your permutation order

- *seed* : is the seed for the random permutation if no pattern is given

To create a permutation order the pattern has to be a list of ordered integers. For example consider we have 3 qubits our map could be [2,1,0]. This would mean that qubit 0 will be mapped to 2, qubit 1 will be mapped to qubit 1 and qubit 0 will be mapped to qubit 2. Note that if you don't include a pattern then the function will generate a random permutation. As such you can set the random seed.

The below code generates 2 examples. The first is an 8 qubit circuit that generates a permutation using the map [7,0,6,1,5,2,4,3]. This will map the following:

- Qubit 0 to Qubit 7

- Qubit 1 to Qubit 0

- Qubit 2 to Qubit 6

- Qubit 3 to Qubit 1

- Qubit 4 to Qubit 5

- Qubit 5 to Qubit 2

- Qubit 6 to Qubit 4

- Qubit 7 to Qubit 3

To see the permutation happen qubits 0-3 are initialised to 1 using a Pauli X gate. The second example does not include an actual pattern. As such a random pattern is generated.

36.3 How to run the program

- Copy and paste the code below in to a python file

- Enter your API token in the IBMQ.enable_account('Insert API token here') part

- Save and run

36.4 Output

```
from qiskit import QuantumRegister, ClassicalRegister
from qiskit import QuantumCircuit, execute,IBMQ
from qiskit.circuit.library import Permutation
from qiskit.tools.monitor import job_monitor

IBMQ.enable_account('ENTER API Key HERE')
provider = IBMQ.get_provider(hub='ibm-q')

backend = provider.get_backend('ibmq_qasm_simulator')


q = QuantumRegister(8, 'q')
c = ClassicalRegister(8, 'c')

########## PERMUTATION WITH PATTERN 7,0,6,1,5,2,4,3
circuit = QuantumCircuit(q, c)

circuit.x(q[0])
circuit.x(q[1])
circuit.x(q[2])
circuit.x(q[3])
```

```
circuit += Permutation(num_qubits = 8, pattern =
    [7,0,6,1,5,2,4,3])

circuit.measure(q, c)

job = execute(circuit, backend, shots=100)
job_monitor(job)

counts = job.result().get_counts()

print(circuit)
print(counts)

####### RANDOM PERMUTATION CIRCUIT
circuit = QuantumCircuit(q, c)

circuit.x(q[0])
circuit.x(q[1])
circuit.x(q[2])
circuit.x(q[3])

circuit += Permutation(num_qubits = 8)

circuit.measure(q, c)

job = execute(circuit, backend, shots=100)
job_monitor(job)

counts = job.result().get_counts()

print(circuit)
print(counts)
```

36.5 Output

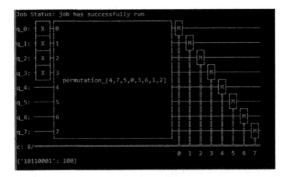

Figure 36.1: Output of the code showing a randomly generated permutation circuit

37 Qiskit: Quantum Machine Learning with QSVM

In this chapter we will explore how to implement a Quantum Support Vector Machine (QSVM) machine learning method on IBM's Quantum computers using Qiskit.

37.1 What is a Support Vector Machine?

A support vector machine is a supervised machine learning method that is trained using a dataset and will predict if a particular observation is in a certain class based upon what it has been trained on. It is similar to a linear classifier in that it uses a hyperplane to separate classes.

However along with the hyperplane support vectors are used. These are essentially data points that are used to maximise the margin and thus the distance between the classes. However the Quantum Support Vector Machine is different in that it uses a feature map to map data points to a quantum circuit.

37.2 Implementation

First we will need to specify the backend device that we will send the job too.

```
IBMQ.enable_account('ENTER API KEY HERE')
provider = IBMQ.get_provider(hub='ibm-q')

backend = provider.get_backend('ibmq_qasm_simulator')
```

Here we specify ibmq_qasm_simulator which is just a classical simulator however you can find which quantum devices are running using:

```
backend_overview()
```

To implement the QSVM we first need to have a training dataset. In this tutorial we are using a gene expression dataset from the RNA-Seq Nexus from Smokers and Non-smokers and use the gene expression of CDKN2A as the feature.

With this we can predict if the observation is from a non-smoker or a smoker based upon the gene expression of CDKN2A.

The easiest way to implement the dataset in through numpy arrays:

```
training_data = {'A': np.asarray([[0.324],[0.565]]),'B':
    np.asarray([[1.324],[1.565]])}
```

Where A is the numpy array for smokers and B is the array for Non-smokers.

Next we implement a testing dataset. This will be used to test

the accuracy of the QSVM model. It looks exactly the same as
the training dataset.

```
testing_data = {'A': np.asarray([[0.024],[0.456]}), 'B':
    np.asarray([[1.777],[1.341]])
```

Next we specify the number of qubits to be used. Rule of
thumb is N qubits for N features. Since we are using 1 feature
we are using 1 qubit.

```
num_qubits = 1
```

Then we specify the feature map. This maps the data with
second order expansion by entangling qubits. Since we are only
using 1 feature and thus 1 qubit entanglement is not required.

```
feature_map =
    SecondOrderExpansion(feature_dimension=num_qubits,depth=2,
    entanglement='full')
```

In the code above the depth just means the number of times
the circuit will repeat. This is normally defaulted to 2. entanglement = 'full' means all qubits will be entangled with each
other.

Figure 37.1: Generated quantum circuit for the QSVM.

In the generated quantum circuit you will see that it consists of only 1 qubit and some unitary gates.

Next we create the QSVM with the following code:

```
svm = QSVM(training_data,testing_data)
```

Then we specify the quantum instance:

```
quantum_instance =
    QuantumInstance(backend,shots=shots,skip_qobj_validation=False)
```

This is just a way to specify the backend as well as the number of shots we want the device to run. skip_qobj_validation=False is used to stop any warnings displaying in the output.

Next we run the QSVM to get the accuracy using the following code. This is where it is sent as a job to the quantum device.

```
result = svm.run(quantum_instance)
```

If we print the result then we will get the accuracy based upon its performance from the testing dataset. However if you want to use the model to predict unlabelled data then you can use the predict function as below:

```
data = np.array([[1.453],[1.023],[0.135],[0.266]])
    #Unlabelled data
prediction = svm.predict(data,quantum_instance)
```

37.3 How to run the program

- Copy and paste the code below in to a python file

- Enter your API token in the IBMQ.enable_account('Insert API token here') part

- Save and run

37.4 Code

```
import numpy as np
from qiskit import BasicAer
from qiskit.aqua import QuantumInstance, aqua_globals
from qiskit.aqua.components.feature_maps import
    SecondOrderExpansion
from qiskit.aqua.components.multiclass_extensions import
    (ErrorCorrectingCode,AllPairs,OneAgainstRest)
from qiskit.aqua.algorithms import QSVM
from qiskit.aqua.utils import get_feature_dimension
from qiskit import IBMQ

print('Quantum SVM')
print('-----------\n')

shots = 8192 # Number of times the job will be run on the
    quantum device

training_data = {'A':
    np.asarray([[0.324],[0.565],[0.231],[0.756],[0.324],
[0.534],[0.132],[0.344]]),
    'B':
    np.asarray([[1.324],[1.565],[1.231],[1.756],[1.324],[1.534],
[1.132],[1.344]])}
```

```
testing_data = {'A':
    np.asarray([[0.024],[0.456],[0.065],[0.044],[0.324]]),
'B': np.asarray([[1.777],[1.341],[1.514],[1.204],[1.135]])}

IBMQ.enable_account('ENTER API KEY HERE')
provider = IBMQ.get_provider(hub='ibm-q')

backend = provider.get_backend('ibmq_qasm_simulator') #
    Specifying Quantum device

num_qubits = 1

feature_map =
    SecondOrderExpansion(feature_dimension=num_qubits,depth=2,
entanglement='full')

svm = QSVM(feature_map, training_data,testing_data) #
    Creation of QSVM

quantum_instance =
    QuantumInstance(backend,shots=shots,skip_qobj_validation=False)

print('Running....\n')

result = svm.run(quantum_instance) # Running the QSVM and
    getting the accuracy results.

data = np.array([[1.453],[1.023],[0.135],[0.266]])
    #Unlabelled data

prediction = svm.predict(data,quantum_instance) # Predict
    using unlabelled data
```

```
print('Prediction of Smoker or Non-Smoker based upon gene
    expression of CDKN2A\n')
print('Accuracy: ' , result['testing_accuracy'],'\n')
print('Prediction from input data where 0 = Non-Smoker and
    1 = Smoker\n')
print(prediction)
```

37.5 Output

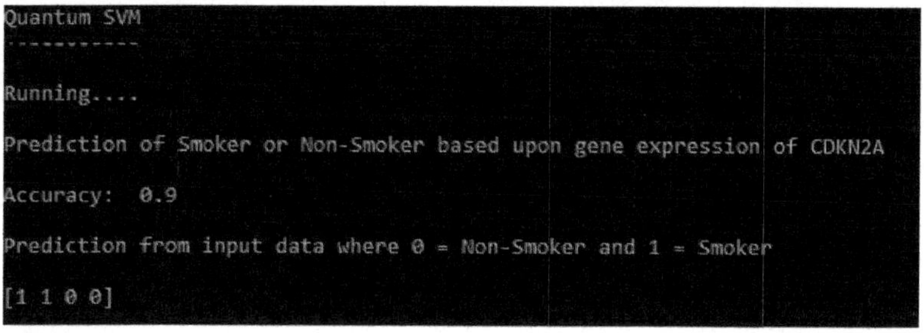

Figure 37.2: Output of the trained QSVM.

38 Quantum Computing in Software Development

This chapter will provide the basic steps needed to successfully implement quantum computing in to a software application that you are developing.

38.1 Step 1: Work out if your application requires quantum computing

Despite quantum computing often being touted as the next big revolution in computing there are many problems where a classical computer can actually outperform a quantum computer. One good example is basic arithmetic. A computer can do arithmetic on the order of nanoseconds due to the fact that they have dedicated logic in the form of ALUs. Quantum computers however have no such dedicated hardware and are quite slow in comparison. Their power does not lay in speed but in the fact that they can make use of quantum parallelisation.

In fact on specific quantum devices called annealing processors it is often better for the runtime to be as slow as possible since if the runtime is too fast the solution will be nonoptimal.

38.2 What types of problems can Quantum Computers solve?

Quantum computers tend to be able to solve problems that have a very high search space. For example, consider a database. Let's say you need to search a database for an entry. The worst case scenario for a classical computer is that it will have to go through the entire database to find the entry you wish to find. This corresponds to a computational complexity of O(N).

However with quantum computing it is possible to solve such problems more efficiently and with less computational complexity. For example a quantum algorithm called Grover's search algorithm can solve the problem in O(N) time.

38.3 Step 2: Find the right quantum device

Now that we have worked out our application can benefit from quantum computing we now need to find the right device. The field of quantum computing is a burgeoning one and as such there have been many different advancements. As a result there have been many different quantum devices developed each with their own pros and cons. As such when developing an application it is important to know which device is best depending on the problem you wish to solve.

38.3.1 Gate based Quantum Computing

The most popular type of quantum device is the gate based quantum computer. This is a quantum computer where operations are done on qubits using quantum logic gates. These logic gates are much like the logic gates found in classical computers but are more complex.

Here are some examples:

Hadamard Gate: This logic gate puts a qubit in to a super-position of states and is arguably the most important quantum logic gate

Pauli gates: These are a set of gates that rotate the qubits state by 180 degrees on different axes. A X-gate rotates the state around the X axis while the Z-gate rotates around the Z axis. There's also a Y-gate that rotates around the Y axis.

Controlled NOT (CNOT): This is a multi qubit gate that operates on a qubit based upon the state of another. If the control qubit is 1 then the target qubits state will be flipped from 0 to 1 or vice versa

Gate based quantum computers are general purpose and such can be used for any problem that requires quantum parallelisation. For example factoring numbers using Shor's algorithm or efficient search using Grover's search algorithm. Machine learning can also be done using variational quantum circuits.

There are many different hardware implementations of gate

based quantum computing:

Superconducting quantum devices: The most popular hardware implementation that use noisy quantum circuits with a qubit count ranging between 5 and 53 qubits. They also tend to have to be cooled using refrigeration.

Trapped ion devices: These use trapped ions as qubits. These devices tend to have very high fidelity qubits with much higher coherence times but a lower qubit count compared to superconducting devices.

Photon based devices: These use photons as qubits. These devices tend to have a high fidelity and fast gate operations and do not require refrigeration.

38.3.2 Quantum Annealers

This type of quantum computer is designed specifically for solving optimisation problems. For example the Travelling Salesman problem which corresponds to finding the most optimal route around a city. On quantum annealers this is done by first initializing the qubits into superposition. After this the qubits and connections between them are slowly tuned such that at the end of runtime the configuration corresponds to the optimal solution of interest.

38.3.3 Picking a device based upon qubit/gate error

Another issue to look at when picking a quantum device is the issue relating to qubit and gate errors. For example superconducting quantum devices are very prone to noise which can lead to errors. These errors come in 3 types (bit flips, phase flips, and readout errors). These can be corrected using quantum error correction/mitigation methods however these may require additional qubits and gates in the quantum circuits.

As such it is best to pick the best device based upon qubit error rates. For example one device may have low fidelity qubits that are prone to error while another may have very high fidelity qubits and as such a lower probability of errors occurring.

38.4 Step 3: Create a quantum algorithm to solve the problem

After you have picked the right device to solve the problem you will have to create a quantum algorithm. In gate based quantum computers this could be a small circuit. For example if you wanted to create a 32 qubit random number generator you would simply create a quantum circuit that initialises 32 qubits into superposition using Hadamard gates. Then you would measure the qubits and the results would be brought back into your application.

Obviously depending on your problem your quantum circuit may be way more complex. Your algorithm may even be hybrid and contain a classical part of the algorithm and a quantum part consisting of a circuit. Some may be variational quantum circuits where the state of the qubit is measured then re-updated each time based upon the problem of interest. In your algorithm you should be making use of either superpositioning or entanglement. These are quantum mechanical effects that allow quantum computers to outperform classical computers. If your algorithm does not make use of either of these then there is a good chance your algorithm will not outperform its classical equivalent. In gate based quantum computing this is easy to check. If your circuit uses Hadamard gates then it is using superpositioning. If your circuit creates bell states with Hadamard gates and multi qubit gates then it is using entanglement.

38.5 Step 4: Test the performance of your quantum algorithm

A common mistake among developers is to create a quantum algorithm that seems to work but does not have a quantum advantage. A quantum advantage can be defined as when a quantum computer can solve a problem much faster than a classical computer. If your quantum algorithm can be beaten by a classical equivalent then there is no point even using your algorithm.

As such it is very important that you test your quantum algorithm against a classical one. If your algorithm has lower performance then use the classical algorithm instead. An application that has a speedup from QC is excellent but if there is no speedup then it is simply a gimmick.

Bibliography

[1] Paul Benioff. The computer as a physical system: A microscopic quantum mechanical Hamiltonian model of computers as represented by Turing machines. *Journal of Statistical Physics*, 22(5):563–591, May 1980.

[2] Charles H. Bennett and Gilles Brassard. Quantum cryptography: Public key distribution and coin tossing. *Theoretical Computer Science*, 560:7–11, Dec 2014.

[3] Charles H. Bennett and Stephen J. Wiesner. Communication via one- and two-particle operators on einstein-podolsky-rosen states. *Phys. Rev. Lett.*, 69:2881–2884, Nov 1992.

[4] Zhengbing Bian, Fabian Chudak, William G. Macready, Lane Clark, and Frank Gaitan. Experimental determination of ramsey numbers. *Physical Review Letters*, 111(13), Sep 2013.

[5] Sergio Boixo, Troels F. Rønnow, Sergei V. Isakov, Zhihui Wang, David Wecker, Daniel A. Lidar, John M. Martinis, and Matthias Troyer. Evidence for quantum annealing with more than one hundred qubits. *Nature Physics*, 10(3):218–224, Feb 2014.

[6] S. L. Braunstein, C. M. Caves, R. Jozsa, N. Linden, S. Popescu, and R. Schack. Separability of Very Noisy

Mixed States and Implications for NMR Quantum Computing. , 83(5):1054–1057, August 1999.

[7] D. Deutsch. Quantum theory, the Church-Turing principle and the universal quantum computer. *Proceedings of the Royal Society of London Series A*, 400(1818):97–117, July 1985.

[8] David Deutsch and Richard Jozsa. Rapid Solution of Problems by Quantum Computation. *Proceedings of the Royal Society of London Series A*, 439(1907):553–558, December 1992.

[9] Richard P. Feynman. Simulating Physics with Computers. *International Journal of Theoretical Physics*, 21(6-7):467–488, June 1982.

[10] Daniel M. Greenberger, Michael A. Horne, and Anton Zeilinger. Going beyond bell's theorem, 2007.

[11] J. A. Jones and M. Mosca. Implementation of a quantum algorithm on a nuclear magnetic resonance quantum computer. *The Journal of Chemical Physics*, 109(5):1648–1653, Aug 1998.

[12] Jonathan A. Jones, Michele Mosca, and Rasmus Hvass Hansen. Implementation of a quantum search algorithm on a quantum computer. *Nature*, 393:344–346, 1998.

[13] M.Coggins. A software method for mitigating single qubit errors on superconducting quantum devices. *Quantum Computing UK*, June 2020.

[14] Y. Nakamura, Yu. A. Pashkin, and J. S. Tsai. Coherent control of macroscopic quantum states in a single-cooper-pair box. *Nature*, 398(6730):786–788, Apr 1999.

Bibliography

[15] Matthew Otten and Stephen K. Gray. Recovering noise-free quantum observables. *Phys. Rev. A*, 99:012338, Jan 2019.

[16] Alejandro Perdomo-Ortiz, Neil Dickson, Marshall Drew-Brook, Geordie Rose, and Alán Aspuru-Guzik. Finding low-energy conformations of lattice protein models by quantum annealing. *Scientific Reports*, 2(1), August 2012.

[17] P.W. Shor. Algorithms for quantum computation: discrete logarithms and factoring. In *Proceedings 35th Annual Symposium on Foundations of Computer Science*, pages 124–134, 1994.

[18] Xin Zhang, Hong Xiang, Tao Xiang, Li Fu, and Jun Sang. An efficient quantum circuits optimizing scheme compared with qiskit, 2018.

Index

Printed in Great Britain
by Amazon

39327850R00155